Mike Holt's

JOURNEYMAN
PRACTICE EXAM

Suitable for all electrical exams based on the NEC® such as:
AMP, ICC, Local/State Examining Boards, Pearson VUE, Prometric, Prov, PSI

Theory • Code • Calculations   Based on the 2017 NEC®

Mike Holt Enterprises
MikeHolt.com • 888.NEC.CODE (632.2633)

NOTICE TO THE READER

The text and commentary in this book is the author's interpretation of the 2017 Edition of NFPA 70®, the *National Electrical Code*®. It shall not be considered an endorsement of or the official position of the NFPA® or any of its committees, nor relied upon as a formal interpretation of the meaning or intent of any specific provision or provisions of the 2017 edition of NFPA 70, *National Electrical Code*.

The publisher does not warrant or guarantee any of the products described herein or perform any independent analysis in connection with any of the product information contained herein. The publisher does not assume, and expressly disclaims, any obligation to obtain and include information other than that provided to it by the manufacturer.

The reader is expressly warned to consider and adopt all safety precautions and applicable federal, state, and local laws and regulations. By following the instructions contained herein, the reader willingly assumes all risks in connection with such instructions.

Mike Holt Enterprises disclaims liability for any personal injury, property or other damages of any nature whatsoever, whether special, indirect, consequential or compensatory, directly or indirectly resulting from the use of this material. The reader is responsible for understanding what a Qualified Person is and determining safety and appropriate actions in all circumstances based on the applicable safety standards such as NFPA70E and OSHA.

The publisher makes no representation or warranties of any kind, including but not limited to, the warranties of fitness for particular purpose or merchantability, nor are any such representations implied with respect to the material set forth herein, and the publisher takes no responsibility with respect to such material. The publisher shall not be liable for any special, consequential, or exemplary damages resulting, in whole or part, from the reader's use of, or reliance upon, this material.

Mike Holt's Journeyman Practice Exam, Based on the 2017 NEC®

Fourth Printing: June 2023

Author: Mike Holt
Technical Illustrator: Mike Culbreath
Cover Design: Bryan Burch
Layout Design and Typesetting: Cathleen Kwas

COPYRIGHT © 2017 Charles Michael Holt
ISBN 978-0-9863534-8-2

Produced and Printed in the USA

All rights reserved. No part of this work covered by the copyright hereon may be reproduced or used in any form or by any means graphic, electronic, or mechanical, including photocopying, recording, taping, or information storage and retrieval systems without the written permission of the publisher. You can request permission to use material from this text by e-mailing Info@MikeHolt.com.

For more information, call 888.NEC.CODE (632.2633), or e-mail Info@MikeHolt.com.

NEC®, NFPA 70®, NFPA 70E® and National Electrical Code® are registered trademarks of the National Fire Protection Association.

This logo is a registered trademark of Mike Holt Enterprises, Inc.

If you are an instructor and would like to request an examination copy of this or other Mike Holt Publications:

Call: 888.NEC.CODE (632.2633) • Fax: 352.360.0983
E-mail: Info@MikeHolt.com • Visit: www.MikeHolt.com/Instructors

You can download a sample PDF of all our publications by visiting www.MikeHolt.com.

I dedicate this book to the
Lord Jesus Christ, *my mentor and teacher.*
Proverbs 16:3

We Care...

Since the day I started my business over 40 years ago, my team and I have been working hard to produce products that get results and to help individuals learn how to be successful. I have built my business on the idea that customers come first and everyone on my team will do everything they possibly can to help you succeed. I want you to know that we value you, and are honored that you have chosen us to be your partner in training.

I believe that you are the future of this industry and that it is you who will make the difference in years to come. My goal is to share with you everything that I know and to encourage you to pursue your education on a continuous basis. I hope that not only will you learn theory, Code, calculations, or how to pass an exam, but that in the process, you will become the expert in the field and the person others know to trust.

We genuinely care about you and are dedicated to providing quality electrical training that will help you take your skills to the next level. Thanks for choosing us for electrical training.

God bless and much success,

"...as for me and my house, we will serve the Lord." [Joshua 24:15]

TABLE OF CONTENTS

Part 1—Electrical Theory

Part 2—*National Electrical Code*®

Part 3—Electrical Calculations

ABOUT THE AUTHOR

Mike Holt—Author

Founder and President
Mike Holt Enterprises
Groveland, Florida

Mike Holt is an author, businessman, educator, speaker, publisher and *National Electrical Code* expert. He has written hundreds of electrical training books and articles, founded three successful businesses, and has taught thousands of electrical *Code* seminars across the U.S. and internationally. His electrical training courses have set the standard for trade education, enabling electrical professionals across the country to take their careers to the next level.

Mike draws on his previous experience as an electrician, an inspector, a contractor and an instructor to guide him in developing powerful training solutions that electricians understand and enjoy. He is always mindful of how hard it can be for students who are intimidated by school, by their feelings towards learning, or by the complexity of the *NEC*. He's mastered the art of explaining complicated concepts in an easy-to-understand way. His extensive use of graphics helps students apply the content and connect the material to their work in the field. This commitment, coupled with the lessons he learned at the University of Miami's MBA program, has helped him build one of the largest electrical training and publishing companies in the United States.

Mike's one-of-a-kind presentation style and his ability to simplify and clarify technical concepts explain his unique position as one of the premier educators and *Code* experts in the country. Mike's ultimate goal has always been to increase electrical safety and improve lives. To that end, he is always looking for the best ways for his students to learn the *Code*, pass electrical exams, and increase their understanding. His passion for the electrical field continues to grow, and today he is more committed than ever to serve the electrical industry.

His commitment to pushing boundaries and setting high standards extends into his personal life. Mike's an eight-time Overall National Barefoot Waterski Champion with more than 20 gold medals, and many national records, and he has competed in three World Barefoot Tournaments. In 2015, at the tender age of 64, he started a new adventure—competitive mountain bike racing. Every day he continues to find ways to motivate himself, both mentally and physically.

Mike and his wife, Linda, reside in New Mexico and Florida, and are the parents of seven children and six grandchildren. As his life has changed over the years, a few things have remained constant: his commitment to God, his love for his family, and doing what he can to change the lives of others through his products and seminars.

Special Acknowledgments

My Family. First, I want to thank God for my godly wife who's always by my side and also for my children.

My Staff. A personal thank you goes to my team at Mike Holt Enterprises for all the work they do to help me with my mission of changing peoples' lives through education. They work tirelessly to ensure that in addition to our products meeting and exceeding the educational needs of our customers, we stay committed to building life-long relationships with them throughout their electrical careers.

The National Fire Protection Association. A special thank you must be given to the staff at the National Fire Protection Association (NFPA), publishers of the *NEC*—in particular, Jeff Sargent for his assistance in answering my many *Code* questions over the years. Jeff, you're a "first class" guy, and I admire your dedication and commitment to helping others understand the *NEC*. Other former NFPA staff members I would like to thank include John Caloggero, Joe Ross, and Dick Murray for their help in the past.

PRACTICE EXAM INSTRUCTIONS

General

This exam is intended to be used as a diagnostic tool to help you evaluate your preparation for taking an exam, and is not intended to be a duplication of any actual licensing exam. We suggest you use this exam to evaluate yourself to determine the areas in which you need to focus your studies to improve your test score. This exam is comprised of three parts:

Part 1—**Electrical Theory** (4-Hour Limit)
Part 2—*National Electrical Code®* (4-Hour Limit)
Part 3—**Electrical Calculations** (5-Hour Limit)

Reference Books

To duplicate the conditions you'll face on your exam, use those reference books which you're permitted to bring into the testing room. You'll find this list of reference materials in the Candidate Booklet provided by the state or the testing agency for your state. If your state does not allow the use of reference books other than the *NEC®*, you should attempt this test using only the *Code* book.

Note: There's not enough time to search for every answer in your book, so try to answer as many questions as possible without looking them up.

DO NOT LOOK AT ANY PART OF THE EXAM UNTIL THE APPROPRIATE TIME IN THE SCHEDULE.

Materials

You'll need a blank sheet of paper, a calculator, approved reference books (see above), several pencils, and an alarm clock or timer.

Grading Your Exam

Your score is important, but keep in mind that your goal in doing this practice exam is to determine your weakest areas so you know what you need to review. To grade your Answer Sheet, go to the Answer Keys beginning on page 35. Grade each Part separately. Use the following formula:

Score (Number Correct Answers) /Total Number of Questions
x 100 = Percentage Correct

Part 1 Score _____ / 100 x 100 = _____%

Part 2 Score _____ / 100 x 100 = _____%

Part 3 Score _____ / 65 x 100 = _____%

Note: Any part of the exam on which you scored less than 75% is considered failing, and additional study is needed. If, after taking these exams you determine that you need to do additional study, *Mike Holt's Electrical Exam Preparation, Electrical Theory,* and *Understanding the National Electrical Code* textbooks and DVDs can provide the training you need to pass the first time.

Time Schedule

The total practice time for these Practice Exams is 13 hours. We suggest that you do not take more than one Part a day. Use an alarm clock or timer to mark your time so that you can stay focused.

Adjust your starting and finish times to allow the same amount of testing time as given in the following examples:

Part 1—Electrical Theory

7:55 a.m.: Have all your materials gathered and ready. Go to Page 51 and tear out the Part 1 Electrical Theory Answer Sheet to record your answers. Set the alarm for 12:00 noon, or set your timer for 4 hours (to mark the end of Part 1).

8:00 a.m.: Go to Page 1, start your timer, and begin Part 1—Electrical Theory Exam. Answer all questions as quickly and accurately as possible.

12:00 noon: Part 1 is over, even if you're not finished.

Part 2—*National Electrical Code*

7:55 a.m.: Go to Page 53 and tear out the Part 2 *National Electrical Code* Answer Sheet to record your answers. Set the alarm for 12:00 noon, or set your timer for 4 hours (to mark the end of Part 2). Use the *NEC* and any other permitted reference books.

8:00 a.m.: Go to Page 13, start your timer, and begin Part 2—*National Electrical Code*. Answer all questions as quickly and accurately as possible. Do NOT start Part 3

12:00 noon: Part 2 is over, even if you're not finished.

Part 3—Electrical Calculations

7:55 a.m.: Go to Page 55 and tear out the Part 3 Electrical Calculations Answer Sheet to record your answers. Set the alarm for 1:00 p.m., or set your timer for 5 hours (to mark the end of Part 3).

8:00 a.m.: Go to Page 25, start your timer, and begin Part 3—Electrical Calculations. Use blank paper to work out the calculations.

1:00 p.m.: Part 3 is over, even if you're not finished.

PART 1

ELECTRICAL THEORY EXAM (4 HOURS)

The questions for this exam are extracted from *Mike Holt's Illustrated Guide to Basic Electrical Theory* textbook.

CHAPTER 1— ELECTRICAL FUNDAMENTALS

UNIT 1—MATTER

1. Providing a path to the earth often helps reduce electrostatic charge.

    (a) True
    (b) False

2. Lightning frequently terminates to a point of elevation and strikes nonmetallic as well as metallic objects with the same frequency.

    (a) True
    (b) False

3. The termination of the lightning stroke is unlikely to ignite combustible materials.

    (a) True
    (b) False

4. Lightning protection is intended to protect the building itself, as well as the electrical equipment on or inside the structure.

    (a) True
    (b) False

UNIT 3—MAGNETISM

5. Nonmagnetic metals are ferrous, meaning they do not contain any iron, and cannot be magnetized.

    (a) True
    (b) False

6. Magnetic lines of force can cross each other and they are called flux lines.

    (a) True
    (b) False

UNIT 4—ELECTRICITY

7. It is not the force of the magnetic field through a conductor that produces electricity; it is the relative motion of the field to the electrons within the conductor that produces the movement of electrons.

    (a) True
    (b) False

8. People become injured and death occurs when voltage pushes electrons through the human body causing the heart to go into ventricular fibrillation.

    (a) True
    (b) False

9. The severity of an electric shock is dependent on the current flowing through the body, which is impacted by circuit voltage and contact resistance.

    (a) True
    (b) False

10. An electrical arc blast can approach _____, which vaporizes metal parts and produces an explosive and deadly pressure wave.

    (a) 10,000°F
    (b) 15,000°F
    (c) 25,000°F
    (d) 30,000°F

UNIT 5—ELECTROMAGNETISM

11. If a conductor carrying current is next to another conductor carrying current in the opposite direction, the electromagnetic field attempts to push the conductors apart.

    (a) True
    (b) False

UNIT 6—USES OF ELECTROMAGNETISM

12. A clamp-on ac ammeter has a coil that is clamped around the conductor and detects the rising and falling _____ field being produced due to the ac flow through the conductor.

    (a) static
    (b) current
    (c) power
    (d) magnetic

13. Ohmmeters measure the _____ or opposition to current flow of a circuit or component.

    (a) voltage
    (b) current
    (c) power
    (d) resistance

14. The megger is used to measure very high-_____ values, such as those found in cable insulation, or motor and transformer windings.

    (a) voltage
    (b) current
    (c) power
    (d) resistance

15. The electric motor works on the principle of the attracting and repelling forces of _____ fields.

    (a) voltage
    (b) current
    (c) power
    (d) magnetic

16. The _____ of a generator is forced to rotate while it is being subjected to the magnetic field of the stator.

    (a) winding
    (b) rotor
    (c) stator
    (d) b or c

17. A holding relay is primarily used for worker convenience.

    (a) True
    (b) False

CHAPTER 2—BASIC ELECTRICITY

UNIT 7—THE ELECTRICAL CIRCUIT

18. According to the Electron Current Flow Theory, electrons flow away from the negative terminal of the source, through the circuit and load, toward the positive terminal of the source.

    (a) True
    (b) False

19. According to the Conventional Current Flow Theory, electrons travel from positive to negative.

    (a) True
    (b) False

UNIT 9—ELECTRICAL FORMULAS

20. The major advantage of alternating current over direct current is that voltage can be changed through the use of a transformer.

    (a) True
    (b) False

21. The best conductors, in order of their conductivity, are gold, silver, copper, and aluminum.

    (a) True
    (b) False

22. In a dc circuit, the only opposition to current flow is the physical resistance of the material. This opposition is called "reactance" and is measured in ohms.

    (a) True
    (b) False

23. What is the voltage drop of two 12 AWG conductors (0.40 ohms) supplying a 16A load, located 100 ft from the power supply? Formula: $E = I \times R$

    (a) 1.60V
    (b) 3.20V
    (c) 6.40V
    (d) 12.80V

24. What is the resistance of the circuit conductors when the conductor voltage drop is 7.20V and the current flow is 50A?

    (a) 0.14 ohms
    (b) 0.30 ohms
    (c) 3 ohms
    (d) 14 ohms

25. What is the power loss in watts of a conductor that carries 24A and has a voltage drop of 7.20V?

    (a) 175W
    (b) 350W
    (c) 700W
    (d) 2,400W

26. What is the approximate power consumed by a 10 kW heat strip rated 230V, when connected to a 208V circuit?

    (a) 8.2 kW
    (b) 9.5 kW
    (c) 11.3 kW
    (d) 12.4 kW

27. The formulas in the formula wheel apply to _____.

    (a) dc
    (b) ac with unity power factor
    (c) dc or ac circuits
    (d) a and b

28. The total circuit resistance of two 12 AWG conductors (each 100 ft long) is 0.40 ohms. If the current of the circuit is 16A, what is the power loss of the conductors in watts?

    (a) 75W
    (b) 100W
    (c) 300W
    (d) 600W

29. What is the conductor power loss in watts for a 120V circuit that has a 3 percent voltage drop and carries a current flow of 12A?

    (a) 43W
    (b) 86W
    (c) 172W
    (d) 1,440W

30. What does it cost per year (at 8 cents per kWh) for the power loss of a 12 AWG circuit conductor (100 ft long) that has a total resistance of 0.40 ohm and current flow of 16A?

    (a) $30
    (b) $50
    (c) $70
    (d) $90

31. What is the power consumed by a 10 kW heat strip rated 230V connected to an 115V circuit?

    (a) 2.50 kW
    (b) 5 kW
    (c) 7.50 kW
    (d) 15 kW

CHAPTER 3—BASIC ELECTRICAL CIRCUITS

UNIT 10—SERIES CIRCUITS

32. The opposition to current flow results in voltage drop.

    (a) True
    (b) False

33. Kirchoff's Voltage Law states, "In a series circuit, the sum of the voltage drops across all of the resistors will equal the applied voltage."

    (a) True
    (b) False

34. Kirchoff's Current Law states, "In a series circuit, the current is _____ through the transformer, the conductors, and the appliance."

    (a) proportional
    (b) distributed
    (c) additive
    (d) the same

UNIT 11—PARALLEL CIRCUITS

35. According to Kirchoff's Current Law, the total current provided by the source to a parallel circuit will equal the sum of the currents of all of the branches.

    (a) True
    (b) False

36. The total resistance of a parallel circuit can be calculated by the _____ method.

    (a) equal resistance
    (b) product-over-sum
    (c) reciprocal
    (d) any of these

37. When power supplies are connected in parallel, the voltage remains the same, but the current or amp-hour capacity will be increased.

    (a) True
    (b) False

UNIT 13—MULTIWIRE CIRCUITS

38. A balanced 3-wire, 120/240V, single-phase circuit is connected so that the ungrounded conductors are from different transformer phases (Line 1 and Line 2). The current on the neutral conductor will be _____ percent of the ungrounded conductor current.

    (a) 0
    (b) 70
    (c) 80
    (d) 100

39. If the ungrounded conductors of a multiwire circuit are not terminated to different phases, this can cause the neutral current to be in excess of the neutral conductor rating.

    (a) True
    (b) False

40. The current flowing on the neutral conductor of a multiwire circuit is called "unbalanced current."

    (a) True
    (b) False

41. Improper wiring or mishandling of multiwire branch circuits can cause _____ connected to the circuit.

    (a) overloading of the ungrounded conductors
    (b) overloading of the neutral conductors
    (c) destruction of equipment because of overvoltage
    (d) b and c

42. Because of the dangers associated with an open neutral conductor, the continuity of the _____ conductor cannot be dependent upon the receptacle.

    (a) ungrounded
    (b) neutral
    (c) a and b
    (d) equipment grounding

CHAPTER 4— ELECTRICAL SYSTEMS AND PROTECTION

UNIT 14—THE ELECTRICAL SYSTEM

43. Electrons leaving a power supply are always trying to return to the same power supply; they are not trying to go into the earth.

    (a) True
    (b) False

44. To prevent fires and electric shock, the *NEC* specifies that neutral current can flow on metal parts of the electrical system.

    (a) True
    (b) False

45. Metal parts of premises wiring must be bonded to a low-impedance path designed so that the circuit protection device will quickly open and clear a ground fault.

    (a) True
    (b) False

46. Because of the earth's _____ resistance to current flow, it cannot be used for the purpose of clearing a line-to-case ground fault.

    (a) low
    (b) high
    (c) variable
    (d) unpredictable

UNIT 15—PROTECTION DEVICES

Part A—Overcurrent Protection Devices

47. The purpose of overcurrent protection is to protect the conductors and equipment against excessive or dangerous temperatures because of overcurrent. Overcurrent is current in excess of the rated current of equipment or conductors. It may result from a(n) _____.

    (a) overload
    (b) short circuit
    (c) ground fault
    (d) all of these

48. To protect against electric shock or to prevent a fire, a dangerous _____ must quickly be removed by opening the circuit's overcurrent protection device.

    (a) overload
    (b) short circuit
    (c) ground fault
    (d) all of these

49. Inverse time breakers operate on the principle that as the current decreases, the time it takes for the device to open decreases.

    (a) True
    (b) False

50. The _____ sensing element causes the circuit breaker to open when a predetermined calibration temperature is reached.

    (a) magnetic
    (b) electronic
    (c) thermo
    (d) none of these

51. The magnetic time-delay circuit breaker operates on the solenoid principle where a movable core, held with a spring, is moved by the magnetic field of a(n) _____.

    (a) overload
    (b) short circuit
    (c) ground fault
    (d) b or c

52. Available short-circuit current is the current in amperes available at a given point in the electrical system.

    (a) True
    (b) False

53. Factors that affect the available short-circuit current include transformer _____.

    (a) voltage
    (b) kVA rating
    (c) impedance
    (d) all of these

54. Factors that affect the available short-circuit current include circuit conductor _____.

    (a) material
    (b) size
    (c) length
    (d) all of these

55. Circuit breakers and fuses are intended to interrupt the circuit, and they must have an ampere interrupting rating (AIR) sufficient for the available short-circuit current.

    (a) True
    (b) False

56. If the protection device is not rated to interrupt the current at the available fault values at its listed voltage rating, it can explode while attempting to clear the fault.

    (a) True
    (b) False

57. Equipment must have a(n) _____ current rating that permits the protection device to clear a short circuit or ground fault without extensive damage to the components of the circuit.

    (a) overload
    (b) short-circuit
    (c) ground-fault
    (d) b or c

Part B—Ground-Fault Circuit Interrupters

58. A GFCI is designed to protect persons against electric shock. It operates on the principle of monitoring the imbalance of current between the circuit's _____ conductor.

    (a) ungrounded
    (b) neutral
    (c) equipment
    (d) ungrounded and neutral

59. A GFCI-protection device contains an internal monitor that prevents the device from being turned on if there is a neutral-to-case connection downstream of the device, but this only occurs if there is a load on the circuit.

    (a) True
    (b) False

60. Severe electric shock or death can occur if a person touches the ungrounded and the neutral conductors at the same time, even if the circuit is GFCI-protected.

    (a) True
    (b) False

61. Typically, when a GFCI-protection device fails, the switching contacts remain closed and the device will continue to provide power without GFCI protection.

    (a) True
    (b) False

Part C—Arc-Fault Circuit Interrupters

62. Arcing is defined as a luminous discharge of electricity across an insulating medium. Electric arcs operate at temperatures between _____ and expel small particles of very hot molten material.

    (a) 1,000 and 5,000°F
    (b) 2,000 and 10,000°F
    (c) 5,000 and 15,000°F
    (d) 10,000 and 25,000°F

63. Unsafe arcing faults can occur in one of two ways, as series arcing faults or as parallel arcing faults. The most dangerous is the parallel arcing fault.

    (a) True
    (b) False

64. An AFCI-protection device provides protection from an arcing fault by recognizing the characteristics unique to an arcing fault and by functioning to de-energize the circuit when an arc fault is detected.

    (a) True
    (b) False

CHAPTER 5—ALTERNATING CURRENT

UNIT 16—ALTERNATING CURRENT

65. A nonsinusoidal waveform is created when _____ loads distort the voltage and current sine wave.

    (a) linear
    (b) resistive
    (c) inductive
    (d) nonlinear

66. When describing the relationship between voltage and current, the reference waveform is always _____.

    (a) current
    (b) resistance
    (c) voltage
    (d) none of these

67. The effective value is equal to the peak value _____.

    (a) times 0.707
    (b) times 1.41
    (c) times 2
    (d) times $\sqrt{3}$

UNIT 17—CAPACITANCE

68. Even when power is removed from the circuit, capacitors can store large amounts of energy for a long period of time. They can discharge and arc if inadvertently shorted or grounded out.

    (a) True
    (b) False

69. The opposition offered to the flow of ac current by a capacitor is called "capacitive reactance," which is expressed in ohms and abbreviated _____.

    (a) X_c
    (b) X_L
    (c) Z
    (d) none of these

UNIT 18—INDUCTION

70. The induced voltage in a conductor carrying alternating current opposes the change in current flowing through the conductor. The induced voltage that opposes the current flow is called "_____."

    (a) CEMF
    (b) counter-electromotive force
    (c) back-EMF
    (d) all of these

71. For ac circuits, the ac _____ of a conductor must be taken into consideration.

    (a) eddy currents
    (b) skin effect
    (c) resistance
    (d) all of these

72. The expanding and collapsing magnetic field within the conductor induces a voltage in the conductors (CEMF) that repels the flowing electrons toward the surface of the conductor. This is called "_____."

    (a) eddy currents
    (b) induced voltage
    (c) impedance
    (d) skin effect

73. The total opposition to current flow in ac circuits is called "_____" and measured in ohms.

    (a) resistance
    (b) reactance
    (c) impedance
    (d) skin effect

74. The abbreviation for impedance is _____.

    (a) X_L
    (b) X_c
    (c) Z
    (d) none of these

75. Self-induced voltage opposes the change in current flowing in the conductor. This is called "inductive reactance" and it is abbreviated _____.

    (a) X_L
    (b) X_C
    (c) Z
    (d) none of these

UNIT 19—POWER FACTOR AND EFFICIENCY

Part A—Power Factor

76. AC inductive or capacitive reactive loads cause the voltage and current to be in-phase with each other.

    (a) True
    (b) False

77. What size transformer is required for a 100A, 240V, single-phase noncontinuous load that has a power factor of 85 percent?

    (a) 15 kVA
    (b) 25 kVA
    (c) 37.50 kVA
    (d) 50 kVA

78. How many 20A, 120V circuits are required for forty-two, 300W luminaires (noncontinuous load) that have a power factor of 85 percent?

    (a) 4 circuits
    (b) 5 circuits
    (c) 7 circuits
    (d) 8 circuits

Part B—Efficiency

79. If the output is 1,600W and the equipment is 88 percent efficient, what are the input amperes at 120V?

    (a) 10A
    (b) 15A
    (c) 20A
    (d) 25A

CHAPTER 6—MOTORS, GENERATORS, AND TRANSFORMERS

UNIT 20—MOTORS

Part A—Motor Basics

80. Dual-voltage ac motors are made with two field windings. The field windings are connected in _____ for low-voltage operation and in _____ for high-voltage operation.

    (a) series, parallel
    (b) parallel, series
    (c) series, series
    (d) parallel, parallel

81. The motor FLA rating is used when sizing motor conductor size or circuit protection.

    (a) True
    (b) False

82. What is the nameplate FLA for a 20 hp, 208V, three-phase motor with 90 percent power factor and 80 percent efficiency?

    (a) 51A
    (b) 58A
    (c) 65A
    (d) 80A

83. When a motor starts, the current drawn is approximately _____ times the motor FLA; this is known as "motor locked-rotor amperes" (LRA).

    (a) 0.80
    (b) 1.25
    (c) 3
    (d) 6

84. If the rotating part of the motor winding is jammed so that it cannot rotate, no CEMF will be produced in the motor winding. Result—the motor operates at _____ and the windings will be destroyed by excessive heat.

    (a) FLA
    (b) FLC
    (c) LRC
    (d) any of these

85. In an ac induction motor, the stator produces a rotating magnetic field that induces current in the rotor windings. The rotor current generates a magnetic field in opposition to the magnetic field of the stator, thereby causing the rotor to turn.

    (a) True
    (b) False

86. In a(n) _____ motor, the rotor is locked in step with the rotating stator field and is dragged along at the speed of the rotating magnetic field.

    (a) wound-rotor
    (b) induction
    (c) synchronous
    (d) squirrel-cage

87. _____ motors are fractional horsepower motors that operate equally well on ac and dc and are used for vacuum cleaners, electric drills, mixers, and light household appliances.

    (a) AC
    (b) Universal
    (c) Wound-rotor
    (d) Synchronous

88. Swapping _____ of the line conductors can reverse a three-phase ac motor's rotation.

    (a) one
    (b) two
    (c) three
    (d) four

89. The _____ of an ac generator contains the electromagnetic field, which cuts through the stationary conductor coils.

    (a) stator
    (b) rotor
    (c) coil
    (d) winding

90. Three-phase ac generators have three equally spaced windings, _____ out-of-phase with each other.

    (a) 90°
    (b) 120°
    (c) 180°
    (d) 360°

91. The energy transfer ability of a transformer is accomplished because the primary electromagnetic lines of force induce a voltage in the secondary winding.

    (a) True
    (b) False

92. Voltage induced in the secondary winding of a transformer is dependent on the number of secondary turns as compared to the number of primary turns.

    (a) True
    (b) False

93. Wasteful circulating _____ in the iron core cause(s) the core to heat up without any useful purpose.

    (a) conductor resistance
    (b) flux leakage
    (c) eddy currents
    (d) hysteresis losses

94. _____ can be reduced by dividing the core into many flat sections or laminations.

    (a) Conductor resistance
    (b) Flux leakage
    (c) Eddy currents
    (d) Hysteresis losses

95. As current flows through the transformer, the iron core is temporarily magnetized. The energy required to realign the core molecules to the changing electromagnetic field is called "_____" loss.

    (a) conductor resistance
    (b) flux leakage
    (c) eddy currents
    (d) hysteresis

96. Three-phase, _____, wye-connected systems can overheat because of circulating odd triplen harmonic currents.

    (a) 2-wire
    (b) 3-wire
    (c) 4-wire
    (d) none of these

97. The heating from harmonic currents is proportional to the square of the harmonic current.

    (a) True
    (b) False

98. Because of conductor resistance, flux leakage, eddy currents, and hysteresis losses, not all of the input power is transferred to the secondary winding for useful purposes.

    (a) True
    (b) False

99. If the primary phase voltage is 480V and the secondary phase voltage is 240V, the turns ratio is _____.

    (a) 1:2
    (b) 1:41
    (c) 2:1
    (d) 4:1

100. Transformers are rated in _____.

    (a) VA
    (b) kW
    (c) W
    (d) kVA

Suggested Study Materials:

Only when you truly know electrical theory can you have confidence in the practical aspects of your electrical work. Mike Holt's **Electrical Theory Video Training Program** will give you the foundation you need to pass this portion of your exam. This program includes videos and *Mike Holt's Illustrated Guide to Electrical Theory* textbook; it will help you understand what electricity is, how it's used and how it's produced. You'll learn everything from a brief study of matter to a breakdown of circuits for controls, fire alarms, security and much more. You'll also learn the basics for motors and transformers. The full-color textbook provides hundreds of illustrated graphics, detailed examples, and practice questions to give you the training and practice you need to build your understanding of electrical theory.

Visit www.MikeHolt.com/Theory or call 888.632.2633.

Notes

Please use the 2017 *Code* book to answer the following questions. If you need a copy of the *Code* book, visit www.MikeHolt.com/Code or call 888.632.2633

1. Type AC cable is permitted in _____.

   (a) wet locations
   (b) cable trays
   (c) exposed installations
   (d) b and c

2. Listed FMC and LFMC shall contain an equipment grounding conductor if the raceway is installed for the reason of _____.

   (a) physical protection
   (b) flexibility after installation
   (c) minimizing transmission of vibration from equipment
   (d) b or c

3. Cable _____ made and insulated by approved methods can be located within a cable tray provided they are accessible, and do not project above the side rails where the splices are subject to physical damage.

   (a) connections
   (b) jumpers
   (c) splices
   (d) conductors

4. In one- and two-family dwellings where it is not practicable to achieve an overall maximum bonding conductor or equipment grounding conductor length of _____ ft for CATV, a separate grounding electrode as specified in 250.52(A)(5), (A)(6), or (A)(7) shall be used.

   (a) 5
   (b) 8
   (c) 10
   (d) 20

5. An effective ground-fault current path is an intentionally constructed, low-impedance electrically conductive path designed and intended to carry current during a ground-fault condition from the point of a ground fault on a wiring system to _____.

   (a) ground
   (b) earth
   (c) the electrical supply source
   (d) none of these

6. If more than one luminaire is installed on a branch circuit that is not of the multiwire type, a disconnecting means is not required for every luminaire when the light switch for the space ensures that some of the luminaires in the space will still provide illumination.

   (a) True
   (b) False

7. When separate equipment grounding conductors are provided in panelboards, a _____ shall be secured inside the cabinet.

   (a) grounded conductor
   (b) terminal lug
   (c) terminal bar
   (d) none of these

8. The conductors connected to the direct-current input of an inverter for PV systems form the _____.

   (a) branch circuit
   (b) feeder
   (c) inverter input circuit
   (d) inverter output circuit

9. An electric-discharge or LED luminaire or listed assembly can be cord connected if the luminaire is located _____ the outlet, the cord is visible for its entire length except at terminations, and the cord is not subject to strain or physical damage.

   (a) within
   (b) directly below
   (c) directly above
   (d) adjacent to

10. If the use of multiple grounding connections results in objectionable current and the requirements of 250.4(A)(5) or (B)(4) are met, it shall be permitted to _____.

   (a) discontinue one or more but not all of such grounding connections
   (b) change the locations of the grounding connections
   (c) interrupt the continuity of the conductor or conductive path causing the objectionable current
   (d) any of these

11. All 15A or 20A, 120V branch circuits that supply outlets or devices in dwelling unit kitchens, family rooms, dining rooms, living rooms, parlors, libraries, dens, bedrooms, sunrooms, recreation rooms, closets, hallways, laundry areas, or similar rooms or areas shall be AFCI protected by a listed arc-fault circuit interrupter.

   (a) True
   (b) False

12. At least one wall switch-controlled lighting outlet shall be installed in every habitable room, kitchen, and bathroom of a dwelling unit.

   (a) True
   (b) False

13. The insulation temperature rating of conductors in Type NM cable shall be _____.

   (a) 60 degrees C
   (b) 75 degrees C
   (c) 90 degrees C
   (d) 105 degrees C

14. Disconnecting means for air-conditioning or refrigerating equipment can be installed _____ the air-conditioning or refrigerating equipment, but not on panels that are designed to allow access to the equipment, and not over the equipment nameplate.

   (a) on
   (b) within
   (c) a or b
   (d) none of these

15. Each strap containing one or more devices shall count as a _____ volume allowance in accordance with Table 314.16(B), based on the largest conductor connected to a device(s) or equipment supported by the strap.

   (a) single
   (b) double
   (c) triple
   (d) none of these

16. Utilization equipment weighing not more than 6 lb can be supported to any box or plaster ring secured to a box, provided the equipment is secured with at least two _____ or larger screws.

   (a) No. 6
   (b) No. 8
   (c) No. 10
   (d) any of these

17. Threadless couplings approved for use with IMC in wet locations shall be _____.

    (a) rainproof
    (b) listed for wet locations
    (c) moistureproof
    (d) concrete-tight

18. Type _____ cable is a factory assembly of conductors with an overall covering of nonmetallic material suitable for direct burial in the earth.

    (a) NM
    (b) UF
    (c) SE
    (d) TC

19. PVC conduit shall be securely fastened within _____ in. of each box.

    (a) 6
    (b) 12
    (c) 24
    (d) 36

20. Exposed optical fiber cables shall be supported by the building structure using hardware including straps, staples, cable ties, hangers, or similar fittings designed and installed so as not to damage the cable.

    (a) True
    (b) False

21. For cord-and-plug-connected household electric ranges, an attachment plug and receptacle connection at the rear base of the range can serve as the disconnecting means, if it is _____ and meets the intent of 422.33(A).

    (a) less than 40A
    (b) a flush-mounted receptacle
    (c) GFCI-protected
    (d) accessible from the front by the removal of a drawer

22. Snap switches in listed assemblies are not required to be connected to an equipment grounding conductor if _____.

    (a) the device is provided with a nonmetallic faceplate that cannot be installed on any other type of device and the device does not have mounting means to accept other configurations of faceplates
    (b) the device is equipped with a nonmetallic yoke
    (c) all parts of the device that are accessible after installation of the faceplate are manufactured of nonmetallic material
    (d) all of these

23. In patient care spaces, luminaires more than _____ ft above the floor and switches located outside of the patient care vicinity shall be permitted to be connected to an equipment grounding return path complying with 517.13(A) or (B).

    (a) 7
    (b) 7½
    (c) 7¾
    (d) 8

24. Each sign and outline lighting system shall be controlled by an externally operable switch or circuit breaker that opens all ungrounded conductors simultaneously on _____ branch circuits.

    (a) 15A
    (b) 20A
    (c) multiwire
    (d) outdoor

25. _____ are designed for surface mounting and have swinging doors or covers secured directly to and telescoping with the walls of the enclosure.

    (a) Outlet boxes
    (b) Cabinets
    (c) Cutout boxes
    (d) none of these

26. Cable tray systems shall not be used _____.

    (a) in hoistways
    (b) where subject to severe physical damage
    (c) in hazardous (classified) locations
    (d) a or b

27. Receptacle outlets for mobile and manufactured homes are not allowed to be installed ____.

    (a) within or directly over a bathtub or shower space
    (b) in a face-up position in any countertop
    (c) underneath the skirting of the home
    (d) a and b

28. The disconnecting means for a motor controller shall be designed so that it cannot ____ automatically.

    (a) open
    (b) close
    (c) restart
    (d) shut down

29. The number of conductors permitted in LFNC shall not exceed the percentage fill specified in ____.

    (a) Chapter 9, Table 1
    (b) Table 250.66
    (c) Table 310.15(B)(16)
    (d) 240.6

30. Where exposed to the weather, raceways enclosing service-entrance conductors shall be ____ for use in wet locations and arranged to drain.

    (a) approved
    (b) listed
    (c) a or b
    (d) none of these

31. Equipment enclosed in a case or cabinet with a means of sealing or locking so that live parts cannot be made accessible without opening the enclosure is said to be "____."

    (a) guarded
    (b) protected
    (c) sealable
    (d) lockable

32. Equipment bonding jumpers on the supply side of the service shall be no smaller than the sizes specified in ____.

    (a) Table 250.102(C)(1)
    (b) Table 250.122
    (c) Table 310.15(B)(16)
    (d) Table 310.15(B)(6)

33. All 125-volt, single-phase, 15A and 20A receptacles installed in ____ for elevators, dumbwaiters, escalators, moving walks, lifts, and chairlifts shall have ground-fault circuit-interrupter protection for personnel.

    (a) machine rooms
    (b) control spaces
    (c) control rooms
    (d) all of these

34. Where a premises wiring system contains feeders supplied from more than one nominal voltage system, each ungrounded conductor of a feeder shall be identified by phase or line and system by ____, or other approved means.

    (a) color coding
    (b) marking tape
    (c) tagging
    (d) any of these

35. In other than dwelling units, GFCI protection shall be provided for all 15A and 20A, 125V, single-phase receptacles installed within ____ ft from the top inside edge of the bowl of a sink.

    (a) 3
    (b) 4
    (c) 5
    (d) 6

36. Communications equipment includes equipment and conductors used for the transmission of ____.

    (a) audio
    (b) video
    (c) data
    (d) any of these

37. Individual meter socket enclosures shall not be considered service equipment but shall be _____ for the voltage and ampacity of the service.

    (a) listed and rated
    (b) labeled and approved
    (c) inspected and rated
    (d) none of these

38. NFPA 780, *Standard for the Installation of Lightning Protection Systems* provides information on the installation of _____ for lightning protection systems [250.4(A)(1)].

    (a) grounding
    (b) bonding
    (c) a and b
    (d) none of these

39. Horizontal runs of IMC supported by openings through framing members at intervals not exceeding 10 ft and securely fastened within 3 ft of terminations shall be permitted.

    (a) True
    (b) False

40. Remote-control circuits for safety-control equipment shall be classified as _____ if the failure of the equipment to operate introduces a direct fire or life hazard.

    (a) Class 1
    (b) Class 2
    (c) Class 3
    (d) Class I, Division 1

41. Where a remote-control device actuates the service disconnecting means, the service disconnecting means shall still be at a readily accessible location either outside the building or structure, or nearest the point of entry of the service conductors.

    (a) True
    (b) False

42. Where conductors are installed in raceways or cables exposed to direct sunlight on or above rooftops, a temperature adder of _____ degrees F shall be added to the outdoor temperature where the conduits are less than 7/8 in. from the rooftop.

    (a) 30
    (b) 40
    (c) 50
    (d) 60

43. For equipment rated 1,200A or more and over 6 ft wide that contains overcurrent devices, switching devices, or control devices, there shall be one entrance to and egress from the required working space not less than 24 in. wide and _____ ft high at each end of the working space.

    (a) 5 ½
    (b) 6
    (c) 6 ½
    (d) 7

44. Where attachment to an equipment grounding conductor does not exist in the receptacle enclosure, a non-grounding-type receptacle(s) shall be permitted to be replaced with a GFCI-type receptacle(s) where supplied through a ground-fault circuit interrupter; however, some cord-and-plug-connected equipment or appliances require an equipment grounding conductor and are listed in 250.114.

    (a) True
    (b) False

45. Communications wires, communications cables, communications raceways, and cable routing assemblies installed in buildings shall be listed except for communications cable not exceeding 50 ft past the point of entry as allowed by 800.48.

    (a) True
    (b) False

46. All equipment intended for use in PV power systems shall be _____ for the PV application.

    (a) field labeled
    (b) listed
    (c) approved
    (d) a or b

47. A dwelling unit containing two 120V laundry branch circuits has a calculated load of _____ VA for the laundry circuits.

    (a) 1,500
    (b) 3,000
    (c) 4,500
    (d) 6,000

48. Listed outlet boxes to support ceiling-suspended fans that weigh more than _____ lb shall have the maximum allowable weight marked on the box.

    (a) 35
    (b) 50
    (c) 60
    (d) 70

49. Ferrous metal raceways and enclosures for grounding electrode conductors shall be bonded at each end of the raceway or enclosure to the grounding electrode or grounding electrode conductor to create a(n) _____ parallel path.

    (a) mechanically
    (b) electrically
    (c) physically
    (d) none of these

50. Conductors are considered outside a building when they are installed _____.

    (a) under not less than 2 in. of concrete beneath a building or structure
    (b) within a building or structure in a raceway encased in not less than a 2 in. thickness of concrete or brick
    (c) in a vault that meets the construction requirements of Article 450, Part III
    (d) any of these

51. Transformers and transformer vaults shall be readily accessible to qualified personnel for inspection and maintenance, except _____.

    (a) dry-type transformers 1,000V or less, located in the open on walls, columns, or structures
    (b) dry-type transformers 1,000V, nominal, or less and not exceeding 50 kVA in hollow spaces of buildings not permanently closed in by structure
    (c) a or b
    (d) none of these

52. _____ shall not be located over the steps of a stairway.

    (a) Disconnect switches
    (b) Overcurrent devices
    (c) Knife switches
    (d) Transformers

53. Exposed live parts on the power distribution block are allowed when the junction box cover is removed.

    (a) True
    (b) False

54. Cables and conductors of two or more power-limited fire alarm circuits can be installed in the same cable, enclosure, cable tray, raceway, or cable routing assembly.

    (a) True
    (b) False

55. For grounded systems, electrical equipment and other electrically conductive material likely to become energized shall be installed in a manner that creates a _____ from any point on the wiring system where a ground fault may occur to the electrical supply source.

    (a) circuit facilitating the operation of the overcurrent device
    (b) low-impedance circuit
    (c) circuit capable of safely carrying the ground-fault current likely to be imposed on it
    (d) all of these

56. A vertical run of 4/0 AWG copper shall be supported at intervals not exceeding _____.

    (a) 40 ft
    (b) 80 ft
    (c) 100 ft
    (d) 120 ft

57. Switches and circuit breakers used as switches shall be installed so that they may be operated from a readily accessible place.

    (a) True
    (b) False

58. When one electrical circuit controls another circuit through a relay or an equivalent device, the first circuit is called a "_____."

    (a) primary circuit
    (b) remote-control circuit
    (c) signal circuit
    (d) controller

59. Equipment or materials to which a label, symbol, or other identifying mark of a product evaluation organization that is acceptable to the authority having jurisdiction has been attached is known as "_____."

    (a) listed
    (b) labeled
    (c) approved
    (d) identified

60. Listed FMC can be used as the equipment grounding conductor if the length in any ground return path does not exceed 6 ft and the circuit conductors contained in the conduit are protected by overcurrent devices rated at _____ or less.

    (a) 15A
    (b) 20A
    (c) 30A
    (d) 60A

61. Fire alarm circuits shall be identified at all terminal and junction locations in a manner that helps prevent unintentional signals on fire alarm system circuits during _____ of other systems.

    (a) installation
    (b) testing and servicing
    (c) renovations
    (d) all of these

62. The provisions of Article 690 apply to solar _____ systems, including inverter(s), array circuit(s), and controller(s) for such systems.

    (a) photoconductive
    (b) PV
    (c) photogenic
    (d) photosynthesis

63. Luminaires shall maintain a minimum clearance from the closet storage space of _____.

    (a) 12 in. for surface-mounted incandescent or LED luminaires with a completely enclosed light source
    (b) 6 in. for surface-mounted fluorescent luminaires
    (c) 6 in. for recessed fluorescent luminaires or recessed incandescent or LED luminaires with a completely enclosed light source
    (d) all of these

64. A grounded conductor shall not be connected to normally non-current-carrying metal parts of equipment on the _____ side of the system bonding jumper of a separately derived system except as otherwise permitted in Article 250.

    (a) supply
    (b) grounded
    (c) high-voltage
    (d) load

65. For a circuit to be considered a multiwire branch circuit, it shall have ____.

  (a) two or more ungrounded conductors with a voltage between them
  (b) a grounded conductor having equal voltage between it and each ungrounded conductor of the circuit
  (c) a grounded conductor connected to the neutral or grounded conductor of the system
  (d) all of these

66. Bends in PVC conduit shall ____ between pull points.

  (a) not be made
  (b) not be limited in degrees
  (c) be limited to 360 degrees
  (d) be limited to 180 degrees

67. Type ____ insulated conductors shall not be subject to the ampacity adjustment provisions of 310.15(B)(3)(c).

  (a) THW-2
  (b) XHHW-2
  (c) THWN-2
  (d) RHW-2

68. For ungrounded systems, noncurrent-carrying conductive materials enclosing electrical conductors or equipment shall be connected to the ____ in a manner that will limit the voltage imposed by lightning or unintentional contact with higher-voltage lines.

  (a) raceway
  (b) earth
  (c) electrical supply source
  (d) none of these

69. The terminal of a wiring device for the connection of the equipment grounding conductor shall be identified by a green-colored, ____.

  (a) not readily removable terminal screw with a hexagonal head
  (b) hexagonal, not readily removable terminal nut
  (c) pressure wire connector
  (d) any of these

70. The *NEC* does not apply to electric utility-owned wiring and equipment ____.

  (a) installed by an electrical contractor
  (b) installed on public property
  (c) consisting of service drops or service laterals
  (d) in a utility office building

71. The 3 VA per-square-foot general lighting load for dwelling units does not include ____.

  (a) open porches
  (b) garages
  (c) unused or unfinished spaces not adaptable for future use
  (d) all of these

72. Where mating dissimilar metals, antioxidant material suitable for the battery connection shall be used where ____ by the battery manufacturer.

  (a) documented
  (b) required
  (c) recommended
  (d) none of these

73. For a grounded system, an unspliced ____ shall be used to connect the equipment grounding conductor(s) and the service disconnect enclosure to the grounded conductor of the system within the enclosure for each service disconnect.

  (a) grounding electrode
  (b) main bonding jumper
  (c) busbar
  (d) insulated copper conductor

74. Electrical equipment with ____ and having low smoke and heat release properties, and associated wiring material suitable for the ambient temperature can be installed within an air-handling space (plenum).

  (a) a metal enclosure
  (b) a nonmetallic enclosure listed for use within an air-handling (plenum) space
  (c) any type of enclosure
  (d) a or b

75. All cut ends of LFMC conduit shall be _____ inside and outside to remove rough edges.

    (a) sanded
    (b) trimmed
    (c) brushed
    (d) any of these

76. Switches and circuit breakers used as switches can be mounted _____ if they are installed adjacent to motors, appliances, or other equipment that they supply and are accessible by portable means.

    (a) not higher than 6 ft 7 in.
    (b) higher than 6 ft 7 in.
    (c) in the mechanical equipment room
    (d) up to 8 ft high

77. Type _____ cable is a factory assembly that encloses two or more insulated conductors within a nonmetallic jacket.

    (a) AC
    (b) MC
    (c) NM
    (d) b and c

78. Unless specifically permitted in 400.10, flexible cables, flexible cord sets, and power-supply cords shall not be used where subject to physical damage.

    (a) True
    (b) False

79. Panelboards equipped with snap switches rated at 30A or less shall have overcurrent protection not exceeding _____.

    (a) 30A
    (b) 50A
    (c) 100A
    (d) 200A

80. *NFPA 70E, Standard for Electrical Safety in the Workplace*, provides guidance, such as determining severity of potential exposure, planning safe work practices, arc-flash labeling, and selecting _____.

    (a) personal protective equipment
    (b) coordinated overcurrent protective devices
    (c) a and b
    (d) none of these

81. Entrances to rooms and other guarded locations containing exposed live parts shall be marked with conspicuous _____ forbidding unqualified persons to enter.

    (a) warning signs
    (b) alarms
    (c) a and b
    (d) none of these

82. Connection of conductors to terminal parts shall ensure a thoroughly good connection without damaging the conductors and shall be made by means of _____.

    (a) solder lugs
    (b) pressure connectors
    (c) splices to flexible leads
    (d) any of these

83. Lampholders shall be constructed, installed, or equipped with shades or guards so that _____ is not subjected to temperatures in excess of 90° C (194° F).

    (a) ferrous material
    (b) the shade or guard
    (c) combustible material
    (d) a or b

84. The point of entrance of a CATV coaxial cable is the point _____ at which the coaxial cable emerges from an external wall or from a concrete floor slab.

    (a) outside a building
    (b) within a building
    (c) on the building
    (d) none of these

85. The minimum radius of a field bend on trade size 1¼ RMC is ____ in.

    (a) 7
    (b) 8
    (c) 10
    (d) 14

86. When PVC conduit extends from the pool light forming shell to a pool junction box for a wet-niche luminaire, an 8 AWG ____ bonding jumper shall be installed in the raceway.

    (a) solid bare
    (b) solid insulated
    (c) stranded insulated
    (d) b or c

87. Edison-base fuseholders shall be used only if they are made to accept ____ fuses by the use of adapters.

    (a) Edison-base
    (b) medium-base
    (c) heavy-duty base
    (d) Type S

88. Grounding electrode conductors or supply-side bonding jumpers or conductors shall not be permitted within raceways containing service conductors

    (a) True
    (b) False

89. When bare conductors are installed with insulated conductors, their ampacities shall be limited to ____.

    (a) 60ºC
    (b) 75ºC
    (c) 90ºC
    (d) the lowest temperature rating for any of the insulated conductors

90. Smooth-sheath Type MC cable with an external diameter not greater than ¾ in. shall have a bending radius not less than ____ times the external diameter of the cable.

    (a) five
    (b) ten
    (c) twelve
    (d) thirteen

91. Where Type NM cable is run at angles with joists in unfinished basements and crawl spaces, it is permissible to secure cables not smaller than ____ AWG conductors directly to the lower edges of the joist.

    (a) two, 6
    (b) three, 8
    (c) three, 10
    (d) a or b

92. Surge protective devices shall be listed.

    (a) True
    (b) False

93. Type TC cable shall be permitted to be direct buried, where ____ for such use.

    (a) identified
    (b) approved
    (c) listed
    (d) labeled

94. Luminaires and equipment shall be mechanically connected to an equipment grounding conductor as specified in 250.118 and shall be sized in accordance with ____.

    (a) Table 250.66
    (b) Table 250.122
    (c) Table 310.16
    (d) a and c

95. Metal components shall not be required to be connected to the equipment grounding conductor or supply-side bonding jumper where the metal components are _____.

    (a) installed in a run of nonmetallic raceway(s) and isolated from possible contact by a minimum cover of 18 in. to any part of the metal components
    (b) part of an installation of nonmetallic raceway(s) and are isolated from possible contact to any part of the metal components by being encased in not less than 2 in. of concrete
    (c) a or b
    (d) none of these

96. Type NM cable shall closely follow the surface of the building finish or running boards when run exposed.

    (a) True
    (b) False

97. When installing auxiliary electrodes, the earth shall not be used as an effective ground-fault current path.

    (a) True
    (b) False

98. Plug fuses of the Edison-base type shall be used only _____.

    (a) where overfusing is necessary
    (b) as a replacement in existing installations
    (c) as a replacement for Type S fuses
    (d) if rated 50A and above

99. Accepted industry workmanship practices are described in ANSI/NECA 1-2015, *Standard for Good Workmanship in Electrical Construction*, and other ANSI-approved installation standards.

    (a) True
    (b) False

100. Nominal battery voltage, as it relates to storage batteries, is the value of a(n) _____ of a given voltage class for convenient designation.

    (a) cell or battery
    (b) container
    (c) electrolyte
    (d) intertier connector

Suggested Study Materials:

You'll gain confidence in understanding the *National Electrical Code* when you choose Mike's **Understanding the *NEC* Complete Training Library**. This program is based on Mike's best-selling *Understanding the National Electrical Code Volume 1* and *2* textbooks and videos, and also includes the *NEC Exam Practice Questions* workbook. You'll learn General Requirements, Wiring and Protection, Grounding and Bonding, Wiring Methods and Materials, Equipment for General Use, Special Occupancies, Special Equipment, and Limited Energy and Communications Systems in a very easy-to-understand format that makes this program effective. The videos follow the text as Mike and a panel of experts analyze each section of the Code, and how it applies in the real world.

Visit www.MikeHolt.com/Code or call 888.632.2633.

ELECTRICAL CALCULATIONS EXAM (5 HOURS)

The questions in this part relate directly to *Mike Holt's Illustrated Guide to Electrical Exam Preparation* textbook.

CHAPTER 1—ELECTRICAL THEORY

UNITS 1 THROUGH 4— ELECTRICAL THEORY

Figure 1 applies to Questions 1 through 3.

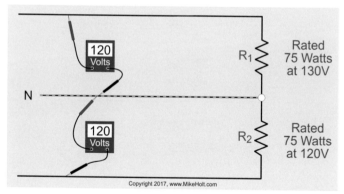

Figure 1

1. The resistance of R_1 is _____.

    (a) 19.20 ohms
    (b) 22.50 ohms
    (c) 192 ohms
    (d) 225 ohms

2. The current of Lamp 2 (R_2) is _____ amperes.

    (a) 0.54
    (b) 0.63
    (c) 5.40
    (d) 6.30

3. The total power consumed of both circuits combined will be _____ watts.

    (a) 139
    (b) 150
    (c) 278
    (d) 300

Figure 2 applies to Questions 4 and 5.

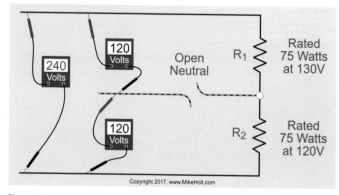

Figure 2

4. If the neutral path is opened as shown in Figure 2, the current of the circuit will be _____ amperes.

    (a) 0.58
    (b) 0.63
    (c) 0.93
    (d) a and b

5. If the neutral is open as shown in Figure 2, what is the voltage drop across the 120V rated bulb (R₂)?

    (a) 110V
    (b) 115V
    (c) 120V
    (d) 240V

Figure 3 applies to Questions 6 through 10:

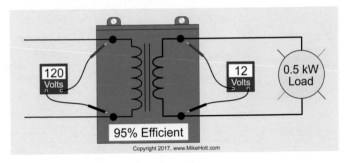

Figure 3

6. The secondary power is closest to _____ VA.

    (a) 475
    (b) 500
    (c) 526
    (d) 550

7. If this transformer is 100 percent efficient, the primary current will be _____ amperes.

    (a) 3.56
    (b) 4.16
    (c) 4.39
    (d) 4.42

8. The primary power is closest to _____ VA.

    (a) 475
    (b) 500
    (c) 526
    (d) 550

9. The primary current of the transformer is approximately _____ amperes, at 95 percent efficiency.

    (a) 0.416
    (b) 3.56
    (c) 4.32
    (d) 4.38

10. The resistance of the load can be found by the formula R = _____.

    (a) E^2/P
    (b) E^2/I
    (c) P/I
    (d) I^2R

Figure 4 applies to Questions 11 and 12.

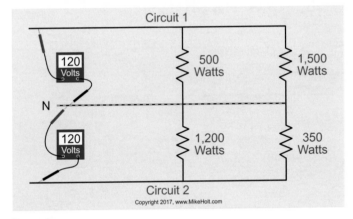

Figure 4

11. The resistance of a 500W, 120V load is approximately _____ ohms.

    (a) 9.60
    (b) 12
    (c) 20
    (d) 28.80

12. What is the total load of Circuit 1?

    (a) 500 watts
    (b) 1,500 watts
    (c) 2,000 watts
    (d) 3,200 watts

CHAPTER 2—*NEC* CALCULATIONS

UNIT 5—RACEWAY AND BOX CALCULATIONS

13. Can a round 4 x ½ in. box marked as 8 cu in. with manufactured cable clamps supplied with 14/2 NM be used with a luminaire that has two 18 AWG fixture wires and a canopy cover?

    (a) Yes
    (b) No

14. What size outlet box is required for one 12/2 NM cable that terminates on a switch, one 12/3 NM cable that terminates on a receptacle, and the box has manufactured cable clamps?

    (a) 4 x 1¼ square
    (b) 4 x 1½ square
    (c) 4 x 2⅛ square
    (d) none of these

15. How many 14 AWG conductors can be pulled through a 4 x 1½ square box with a plaster ring of 3.60 cu in.? The box contains two duplex receptacles, five 14 AWG conductors, and two equipment grounding conductors.

    (a) 1
    (b) 2
    (c) 3
    (d) 4

The following information applies to Questions 16 through 18: A junction box has two trade size 3 raceways entering on the left side. The conductors from one of these leave the top of the box in a trade size 3 raceway in an angle pull. The conductors from the second trade size 3 on the left wall are pulled straight through one of the trade size 2 raceways on the right. Two trade size 2 raceways enter from the right side and two trade size 3 raceways enter from the bottom. All raceways entering the bottom are angle pulls. Figure 5

16. What is the distance from the left wall to the right wall?

    (a) 18 in.
    (b) 20 in.
    (c) 21 in.
    (d) 24 in.

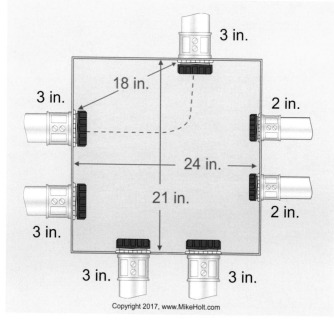

Copyright 2017, www.MikeHolt.com

Figure 5

17. What is the distance from the bottom wall to the top wall?

    (a) 15 in.
    (b) 18 in.
    (c) 21 in.
    (d) 24 in.

18. What is the distance between the raceways that contain the same conductors?

    (a) 15 in.
    (b) 18 in.
    (c) 21 in.
    (d) 24 in.

19. How many 16 TFFN conductors can be installed in trade size ¾ electrical metallic tubing?

    (a) 26
    (b) 29
    (c) 30
    (d) 40

20. How many 1/0 XHHW conductors can be installed in a trade size 2 flexible metal conduit?

    (a) 6
    (b) 7
    (c) 13
    (d) 16

21. If we have a trade size 2 rigid metal conduit and we want to install three THHN compact conductors, what is the largest compact conductor permitted to be installed?

    (a) 4/0 AWG
    (b) 250 kcmil
    (c) 350 kcmil
    (d) 500 kcmil

22. What is the cross-sectional area in sq in. for 10 THW?

    (a) 0.0172
    (b) 0.0243
    (c) 0.0252
    (d) 0.0278

23. What is the cross-sectional area in sq in. for an 8 AWG bare solid conductor?

    (a) 0.013
    (b) 0.027
    (c) 0.038
    (d) 0.045

24. A 200A feeder installed in Schedule 40 rigid nonmetallic conduit has three 3/0 THHN, one 2 THHN, and one 6 THHN. What trade size raceway is required?

    (a) 2
    (b) 2½
    (c) 3
    (d) 3½

25. What trade size rigid metal nipple is required for three 4/0 THHN, one 1/0 THHN, and one 4 THHN?

    (a) 1½
    (b) 2
    (c) 2½
    (d) 3

26. An existing trade size ¾ rigid metal nipple contains four 10 THHN and one 10 AWG (bare stranded) ground wire. How many additional 10 THHN conductors can be installed?

    (a) 5
    (b) 7
    (c) 9
    (d) 11

UNIT 6—CONDUCTOR SIZING AND PROTECTION CALCULATIONS

27. A 2 TW conductor is installed in a location where the ambient temperature is expected to be 102°F. The temperature correction factor for conductor ampacity in this location is _____.

    (a) 0.71
    (b) 0.82
    (c) 0.88
    (d) 0.96

28. The ampacity of six current-carrying 4/0 XHHW aluminum conductors installed in a ground floor slab (wet location) is _____.

    (a) 135A
    (b) 144A
    (c) 185A
    (d) 210A

29. The ampacity of 15 current-carrying 10 RHW aluminum conductors in an ambient temperature of 75°F is _____.

    (a) 12A
    (b) 16A
    (c) 22A
    (d) 30A

30. A(n) _____ THHN conductor is required for a 19.70A load if the ambient temperature is 75°F and there are nine current-carrying conductors in the raceway.

    (a) 8
    (b) 10
    (c) 12
    (d) 14

31. The ampacity of nine current-carrying 10 THW conductors installed in a 20 in. long raceway is _____.

    (a) 25A
    (b) 30A
    (c) 35A
    (d) 40A

UNIT 7—VOLTAGE-DROP CALCULATIONS

32. What is the ac ohms-to-neutral resistance for 100 ft of 3 AWG copper conductor?

    (a) 0.012 ohms
    (b) 0.025 ohms
    (c) 0.33 ohms
    (d) 0.43 ohms

33. A 24A, 240V, single-phase load is located 160 ft from the panelboard. The load is wired with 10 AWG conductors. What is the approximate voltage drop of the branch-circuit conductors?

    (a) 3.20V
    (b) 4.25V
    (c) 5.90V
    (d) 9.50V

34. A single-phase, 5 hp motor is located 110 ft from a panelboard. The nameplate indicates that the voltage is 115/230V and the FLA is 52/26A. What size conductor is required if the motor windings are connected to operate at 115V? Apply the *NEC* recommended voltage-drop limits.

    (a) 10 AWG
    (b) 8 AWG
    (c) 6 AWG
    (d) 3 AWG

35. What is the approximate distance that a single-phase, 7.50 kVA, 240V load can be located from the panelboard so the voltage drop does not exceed 3 percent? The load is wired with 8 AWG copper.

    (a) 55 ft
    (b) 110 ft
    (c) 145 ft
    (d) 220 ft

36. An existing installation consists of 1/0 AWG copper conductors in a nonmetallic raceway to a panelboard located 200 ft from a single-phase, 240V power source. What is the maximum load that can be placed on the panelboard so that the *NEC* recommendations for voltage drop are not exceeded?

    (a) 71A
    (b) 94A
    (c) 109A
    (d) 147A

UNIT 8—MOTOR AND AIR-CONDITIONING CALCULATIONS

37. What size conductor is required for a 5 hp, 230V, single-phase motor? The terminals are rated 75°C.

    (a) 14 AWG
    (b) 12 AWG
    (c) 10 AWG
    (d) 8 AWG

38. Motors with a nameplate service factor (SF) rating of 1.15 or more must have the overload device sized at no more than _____ percent of the motor nameplate current rating.

    (a) 100
    (b) 115
    (c) 125
    (d) 135

39. Motors with a nameplate temperature rise rating not over 40°C must have the overload device sized at no more than _____ percent of motor nameplate current rating.

    (a) 100
    (b) 115
    (c) 125
    (d) 135

40. If a dual-element fuse is used for overload protection, what size fuse is required for a 5 hp, 208V, three-phase motor with a service factor of 1.16, and a motor nameplate current rating of 16A (FLA)?

    (a) 20A
    (b) 25A
    (c) 30A
    (d) 35A

41. Which of the following statements are true for a 10 hp, 208V, three-phase motor with a nameplate current of 29A?

    (a) The branch-circuit conductors can be 8 AWG
    (b) Overload protection is 33A
    (c) Short-circuit and ground-fault protection can be an 80A circuit breaker
    (d) all of these

42. What is the VA input of a dual voltage 5 hp, three-phase motor rated 460/230V?

    (a) 3,027 VA at 460V
    (b) 6,055 VA at 230V
    (c) 6,055 VA at 460V
    (d) b and c

43. The branch-circuit conductors of a 5 hp, 230V motor with a nameplate rating of 25A must have an ampacity of not less than _____. *Note: The motor is used for intermittent duty and, due to the nature of the apparatus it drives, it cannot run for more than five minutes at any one time.*

    (a) 21A
    (b) 23A
    (c) 33A
    (d) 37A

44. The standard overload protection device for a 2 hp, 115V motor that has a full-load current rating of 24A and a nameplate rating of 21.50A must not exceed _____.

    (a) 20.60A
    (b) 24.70A
    (c) 29.90A
    (d) 33.80A

45. The ultimate trip overload device of a thermally protected 1½ hp, 115V motor would be rated no more than _____.

    (a) 23A
    (b) 26A
    (c) 28A
    (d) 31.20A

46. A 2 hp, 115V motor requires a _____ branch-circuit short-circuit protection device. *Note: Use an inverse time breaker for protection.*

    (a) 20A
    (b) 30A
    (c) 40A
    (d) 60A

UNIT 9—DWELLING UNIT CALCULATIONS

The following information applies to Questions 47 through 51:
Laundry circuit of 1,500 VA; two small-appliance circuits are 3,000 VA; ½ hp, 115V motor. Balance these loads on a 115/230V single-phase system, then answer questions 47 through 51.

47. What is the VA of the ½ hp, 115V motor?

   (a) 1,127 VA
   (b) 1,176 VA
   (c) 2,254 VA
   (d) 2,688 VA

48. The total panel load is _____ VA.

   (a) 1,127
   (b) 3,000
   (c) 4,500
   (d) 5,627

49. The total current of both Line 1 and Line 2 equals _____ amperes.

   (a) 30–35
   (b) 36–40
   (c) 41–45
   (d) 46–50

50. The neutral current will be _____ amperes if all loads are on.

   (a) 0 (zero)
   (b) 3
   (c) 10
   (d) 15

51. Under the most severe conditions, the neutral will carry _____ amperes.

   (a) 18.20
   (b) 20
   (c) 23
   (d) 26

52. Balance the following loads and determine the load on the neutral in amperes.

   3,000 VA, 120V small appliance
   1,500 VA, 120V laundry circuit
   1,800 VA, 120V dishwasher
   2,000 VA, 240V dryer
   1,500 VA, 120V disposal.

   (a) 0 (zero)A
   (b) 2.50A
   (c) 3.50A
   (d) 10A

53. What is the feeder/service calculated load for one 6 kW and two 3 kW cooking appliances?

   (a) 4.50 kW
   (b) 4.80 kW
   (c) 6 kW
   (d) 9.30 kW

54. What is the feeder/service calculated load for an 11.50 kW range?

   (a) 6 kW
   (b) 8 kW
   (c) 9.20 kW
   (d) 11.50 kW

55. What is the feeder/service calculated load for a 13.60 kW range?

   (a) 6 kW
   (b) 8 kW
   (c) 8.80 kW
   (d) 9.20 kW

56. How many 15A general-lighting circuits are required for a 2,340 sq ft home?

   (a) 2
   (b) 3
   (c) 4
   (d) 5

57. What is the total calculated load for general lighting and receptacles, and small-appliance and laundry circuits for a 6,540 sq ft dwelling unit before applying demand factors?

    (a) 2,700 VA
    (b) 8,100 VA
    (c) 12,600 VA
    (d) 24,120 VA

58. What is the feeder/service calculated load for one air conditioner (5 hp, 230V) and three baseboard heaters (3 kW)?

    (a) 3,000 VA
    (b) 5,400 VA
    (c) 8,050 VA
    (d) 9,000 VA

59. What is the feeder/service calculated load for a waste disposal (940 VA), dishwasher (1,250 VA), and a water heater (4,500 VA)?

    (a) 5,018 VA
    (b) 6,272 VA
    (c) 6,690 VA
    (d) 8,363 VA

60. What is the feeder/service calculated load for a 4 kW dryer?

    (a) 3 kW
    (b) 4 kW
    (c) 5 kW
    (d) 6 kW

61. What AWG size copper conductors are required for the single-phase 120/240V feeder/service conductors for a dwelling unit with a 190A service calculated load?

    (a) 1/0 AWG
    (b) 2/0 AWG
    (c) 3/0 AWG
    (d) 4/0 AWG

62. The feeder/service neutral load for household cooking appliances such as electric ranges, wall-mounted ovens, or counter-mounted cooking units must be calculated at _____ percent of the calculated load as determined by 220.55.

    (a) 50
    (b) 60
    (c) 70
    (d) 80

63. Both units of a duplex apartment require a 100A main; the resulting 200A service will require _____ copper conductors.

    (a) 1/0 AWG
    (b) 2/0 AWG
    (c) 3/0 AWG
    (d) 4 AWG

64. An 1,800 sq ft residence contains the following: a 4 kW water heater, one 1.50 kW dishwasher, one 4.50 kW dryer, two 3 kW ovens, one 6 kW range, 10 kW of space heat separated in five rooms with thermostats in each room, and one 6 kVA air conditioner. The 120/240V single-phase service for the loads will be _____ when using the optional method of calculation.

    (a) 110A
    (b) 125A
    (c) 150A
    (d) 175A

65. After balancing the following loads, what is the maximum unbalanced neutral current?

    Three 1,900W, 120V lighting loads, and two 2 hp, 115V motors.

    (a) 48A
    (b) 54A
    (c) 57A
    (d) 65A

Suggested Study Materials:

Choose one of Mike's Exam Preparation libraries and you'll find out why his study programs have successfully helped thousands of people pass their exams. Whether you choose his Comprehensive Library that provides a full study program for Theory, Code and Calculations or you choose his streamlined Intermediate Library, you'll find the program that works for you. These programs provide full-color textbooks, and informative videos that will help you pass your exam the first time. For more information, contact our office at 888.632.2633 and we can help you select study materials that fit your needs.

Visit www.MikeHolt.com/ExamPrep or call 888.632.2633.

Notes

1. (a) True

2. (a) True

3. (b) False

4. (b) False

5. (b) False

6. (b) False

7. (a) True

8. (a) True

9. (a) True

10. (d) 30,000° F

11. (a) True

12. (d) magnetic

13. (d) resistance

14. (d) resistance

15. (d) magnetic

16. (b) rotor

17. (b) False

18. (a) True

19. (a) True

20. (a) True

21. (b) False

22. (b) False

23. (c) 6.40V

$E = I \times R$
E = 16A x 0.40 ohms
E = 6.40V

24. (a) 0.14 ohms

$R = E/I$
R = 7.20V/50A
R = 0.14 ohms

25. (a) 175W

$P = I \times E$
P = 24A x 7.20V
P = 172.80W

26. (a) 8.20 kW

The power of the heat strip will be less because the applied voltage (208V) is less than the equipment voltage rating (230V). To calculate this, we must determine the heat strip resistance rating at 230V, and then determine the power rating at 208V based on the heat strip resistance rating.

$P = E^2/R$
E = Applied Voltage = 208V
R = Resistance of Heat Strip = E^2/P
Heat Strip Voltage Rating = 230V
Power Rating of Heat Strip = 10,000W
Resistance of Heat Strip = $230V^2/10,000W$
Resistance of Heat Strip = 5.29 ohms
$P = E^2/R$
P = (208V x 208V)/5.29 ohms
P = 43,624/5.29 ohms
P = 8,178W/1,000
P = 8.20 kW

27. (d) a and b

28. (b) 100W

$P = I^2 \times R$
I = 16A
R = 0.40 ohms
P = (16A x 16A) x 0.40 ohms
P = 102.40W

29. (a) 43W

   P = I x E
   I = 12A
   E = 120V x 3%
   E = 3.60V
   P = 12A x 3.60V
   P = 43.20W

30. (c) $70

   Cost per Year = Power for the Year in kWh x $0.08

   Power per Hour = I² x R
   I = 16A
   R = 0.40 ohms

   Power per Hour = (16A x 16A) x 0.40 ohms
   Power per Hour = 102.40W
   Power for the Year in kWh = (102.40W x 24 hours x
     365 days)/1,000
   Power for the Year in kWh = 897 kWh

   Cost per Year = 897 kWh x $0.08
   Cost per Year = $71.76

31. (a) 2.50 kW

   The power of the heat strip will be less because the applied
   voltage (115V) is less than the equipment voltage rating
   (230V). To calculate this, we must determine the heat strip
   resistance rating at 230V, and then determine the power
   rating at 115V based on the heat strip resistance rating.

   P = E²/R
   E = Applied Voltage = 115V
   R = Resistance of Heat Strip = E²/P
   Heat Strip Voltage Rating = 230V

   Power Rating of Heat Strip = 10,000W
   Resistance of Heat Strip = 230V²/10,000W
   Resistance of Heat Strip = 5.29 ohms

   P = E²/R
   P = 13,225/5.29 ohms
   P = 2,500W/1,000 = 2.50 kW

   *Note: Power changes with the square of the voltage. If the
   voltage is reduced to 50%, then the power consumed will be
   equal to the new voltage percent² or 50%², or 10,000 x (0.50
   x 0.50 = 0.25 = 25%) = 2,500W = 2.50 kW.*

32. (a) True

33. (a) True

34. (d) the same

35. (a) True

36. (d) any of these
37. (a) True
38. (a) 0
39. (a) True
40. (a) True
41. (d) b and c
42. (b) grounded
43. (a) True
44. (b) False
45. (a) True
46. (b) high
47. (d) all of these
48. (d) all of these
49. (b) False
50. (c) thermo
51. (d) b or c
52. (a) True
53. (d) all of these
54. (d) all of these
55. (a) True
56. (a) True
57. (b) short-circuit
58. (d) a and b
59. (b) False
60. (a) True
61. (a) True
62. (c) 5,000 and 15,000° F
63. (a) True
64. (a) True
65. (d) nonlinear
66. (c) voltage
67. (a) times 0.707
68. (a) True
69. (a) X_c
70. (d) all of these
71. (d) all of these
72. (d) skin effect
73. (c) impedance

74. (c) Z

75. (a) X_L

76. (b) False

77. (b) 25 kVA

Load kVA = (Volts x Amperes)/1,000
Load kVA = (240V x 100A)/1,000
Load kVA = 24 kVA

Note: If a question gives you the current, voltage, and power factor, and asks for the VA load, then simply multiply the Volts given by the Amperes given; ignore the Power Factor distractor in the question.

78. (c) 7 circuits

VA per Circuit = Volts x Amperes
VA per Circuit = 120V x 20A
VA per Circuit = 2,400 VA

VA per Luminaire = Watts/Power Factor
VA per Luminaire = 300W/0.85 PF
VA per Luminaire = 353 VA

Lights per Circuit = 2,400 VA/353 VA = 6.80
Lights per Circuit = 6
Circuits = 42 luminaires/6 per circuit
Circuits = 7

79. (b) 15A

Input Watts = Output Watts/Efficiency
Input = 1,600W/0.88 Eff
Input = 1,818W
Input Amperes = Watts/Volts
Input Amperes = 1,818W/120V
Input Amperes = 15.167A

80. (b) parallel, series

81. (b) False

82. (b) 58A

FLA = (Motor hp x 746W)/(E x 1.732 x PF x Eff)
FLA = (20 hp x 746W)/(208V x 1.732 x 0.9 PF x 0.80 Eff)
FLA = 58A

83. (d) 6

84. (c) LRC

85. (a) True

86. (c) synchronous

87. (b) Universal

88. (b) two

89. (b) rotor

90. (b) 120°

91. (a) True

92. (a) True

93. (c) eddy currents

94. (c) Eddy currents

95. (d) hysteresis

96. (c) 4-wire

97. (a) True

98. (a) True

99. (c) 2:1

100. (d) kVA

Notes

Question	Answer	*NEC* Section #
1.	(d)	320.10(1) and (2)
2.	(d)	250.118(5)e
3.	(c)	392.56
4.	(d)	820.100(A)(4) Ex
5.	(c)	100 Effective Ground-Fault Current Path
6.	(a)	410.130(G)(1) Ex 4
7.	(c)	408.40
8.	(c)	690.2 Inverter Input Circuit
9.	(b)	410.62(C)(1)
10.	(d)	250.6(B)(1), (2), and (3)
11.	(a)	210.12(A)
12.	(a)	210.70(A)(1)
13.	(c)	334.112
14.	(c)	440.14
15.	(b)	314.16(B)(4)
16.	(a)	314.27(D) Ex
17.	(b)	342.42(A)
18.	(b)	340.2 Underground Feeder and Branch-Circuit Cable, Type UF
19.	(d)	352.30(A)
20.	(a)	770.24
21.	(d)	422.33(B)
22.	(d)	404.9(B) Ex 2(1), (2), (3), and (4)
23.	(b)	517.13(B)(1) Ex 3
24.	(c)	600.6
25.	(c)	100 Cutout Box
26.	(d)	392.12
27.	(d)	550.13(F)(1) and (2)
28.	(b)	430.103

Question	Answer	*NEC* Section #
29.	(a)	356.22
30.	(c)	230.53
31.	(c)	100 Sealable Equipment
32.	(a)	250.102(C)(1)
33.	(d)	620.85
34.	(d)	215.12(C)(1)(a)
35.	(d)	210.8(B)(5)
36.	(d)	100 Communications Equipment
37.	(a)	230.66
38.	(c)	250.4(A)(1) Note 2
39.	(a)	342.30(B)(4)
40.	(a)	725.31(A)
41.	(a)	230.70(A)(3)
42.	(d)	310.15(B)(3)(c)
43.	(c)	110.26(C)(2)
44.	(a)	406.4(D)(2)(c) Note 2
45.	(a)	800.113(A) and Ex
46.	(d)	690.4(B)
47.	(b)	220.52(B)
48.	(a)	314.27(C)
49.	(b)	250.64(E)(1)
50.	(d)	230.6(1), (2), and (3)
51.	(c)	450.13(A) and (B)
52.	(b)	240.24(F)
53.	(b)	314.28(E)(4)
54.	(a)	760.139(A)
55.	(d)	250.4(A)(5)
56.	(b)	300.19(A) and Table 300.19(A)
57.	(a)	404.8(A)

Question	Answer	*NEC* Section #	Question	Answer	*NEC* Section #
58.	(b)	100 Remote-Control Circuit	79.	(d)	408.36(A)
59.	(b)	100 Labeled	80.	(a)	110.16(B) Note 1
60.	(b)	250.118(5)b	81.	(a)	110.27(C)
61.	(b)	760.30	82.	(d)	110.14(A)
62.	(b)	690.1	83.	(c)	410.97
63.	(d)	410.16(C)(1), (2), (3), and (4)	84.	(b)	820.2 Point of Entrance
64.	(d)	250.30(A)	85.	(b)	344.24 and Chapter 9, Table 2
65.	(d)	100 Branch Circuit, Multiwire	86.	(d)	680.23(B)(2)(b)
66.	(c)	352.26	87.	(d)	240.52
67.	(b)	310.15(B)(3)(c) Ex	88.	(b)	230.7 Ex 1
68.	(b)	250.4(B)(1)	89.	(d)	310.15(B)(4)
69.	(d)	250.126(1), (2), and (3)	90.	(b)	330.24(A)(1)
70.	(c)	90.2(B)(5)a	91.	(d)	334.15(C)
71.	(d)	220.12	92.	(a)	285.6
72.	(c)	480.4(A)	93.	(a)	336.10(10)
73.	(b)	250.24(B)	94.	(b)	410.44
74.	(d)	300.22(C)(3)	95.	(c)	250.86 Ex 3(1) and (2)
75.	(b)	350.28	96.	(a)	334.15(A)
76.	(b)	404.8(A) Ex 2	97.	(a)	250.54
77.	(c)	334.2 Nonmetallic-Sheathed Cable	98.	(b)	240.51(B)
78.	(a)	400.12 and 400.12(7)	99.	(a)	110.12(A) Note
			100.	(a)	480.2 Nominal Voltage (Battery or Cell)

ELECTRICAL CALCULATIONS ANSWER KEY

Note: The calculations are shown immediately following the answers. Methods other than the ones we used may be correct in some cases. If you used a different method of calculation to come up with the same answer, it's probably okay.

1. (d) 225 ohms

   R_1 = Voltage Rating of Lamp²/Power Rating of Lamp
   $R_1 = 130V^2/75W$
   $R_1 = 225$ ohms

2. (b) 0.63

   I_2 = Voltage Rating of Lamp/Resistance Rating of Lamp
   $E = 120V$
   R_2 = Voltage Rating²/Power Rating
   $R_2 = 120V^2/75W$
   $R_2 = 192$ ohms
   $I_2 = E/R_2$
   $I_2 = 120V/192$ ohms
   $I_2 = 0.625A$, rounded to 0.63A

   Reminder: A multiwire circuit with a common neutral is treated as two separate series circuits.

3. (a) 139

   Power Total = $P_1 + P_2$
   $P_1 = E^2/R$
   $P_1 = 120V^2/225$ ohms
   $P_1 = 64W$
   $P_2 = 75W$
   Power Total = 64W + 75W
   Power Total = 139W

Figure 6 applies to Answers 4 and 5:

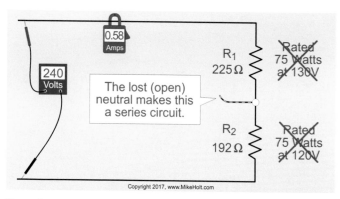

The lost (open) neutral makes this a series circuit.

Copyright 2017, www.MikeHolt.com

Figure 6

4. (a) 0.58

   If neutral is open, the multiwire circuit becomes a 240V series circuit. The current of the circuit is equal to $I = E/R$.
   $E = 240V$ series circuit
   $R_1 = 225$ ohms (answer key question 1)
   $R_2 = 192$ ohms (answer key question 2)
   $I = 240V/(225$ ohms + 192 ohms)
   $I = 240V/417$ ohms
   $I = 0.575A$, rounded to 0.58A

5. (a) 110V

   The voltage across the 120V rated light bulb R_2 is equal to $E_2 = I_T \times R_2$.
   I_T = Voltage Source/Resistance Total
   $I_T = 240V/417$ ohms (answer key question 4)
   $I_T = 0.575A$
   $E_2 = I_T \times R_2$
   $E_2 = 0.575A \times 192$ ohms
   $E_2 = 110V$

6. (b) 500

   Secondary Power 0.50 kVA x 1,000 = 500 VA

7. (b) 4.16

If 100% efficient, the Primary VA is 500.
Primary Current = Primary VA/Primary E
Primary Current = 500 VA/120V = 4.16A

8. (c) 526

Primary Power = Secondary VA/Efficiency
Primary Power = 500 VA/0.95
Primary Power = 526 VA

9. (d) 4.38

Primary Current = Primary VA/Primary Volts
Primary Current = 526 VA/120V
Primary Current = 4.38A

10. (a) E^2/P

11. (d) 28.80 ohms

$R = E^2/P$
R = 120V²/500W
R = 28.80 ohms

12. (c) 2,000 watts

500 watts + 1,500 watts = 2,000 watts

13. (a) Yes

The exception to 314.16(B)(1) permits us to omit fixture wires that enter the outlet box from a luminaire canopy.

Step 1: Determine the number and size of conductors:

14/2 NM cable	2 – 14 AWG
Ground wire	1 – 14 AWG
One cable clamp	1 – 14 AWG

Step 2: Volume of the conductors [Table 314.16(B)]:

4 conductors x 2 cu in. = 8.00 cu in.

14. (c) 4 x 2⅛ square

Step 1: Determine the number and size of conductors:

12/2 NM cable	2 – 12 AWG conductors
12/3 NM cable	3 – 12 AWG conductors
Cable clamps	1 – 12 AWG conductors
Switch	2 – 12 AWG conductors
Receptacles	2 – 12 AWG conductors
Ground wire	1 – 12 AWG conductor
Total Number	11 – 12 AWG conductors

Step 2: Determine the volume (cubic inches) of the above conductors [Table 314.16(B)]:

11 conductors x 2.25 = 24.75 cu in.

Step 3: Select the outlet box from Table 314.16(A):

4 x 2⅛ in. square = 30.30 cu in.

15. (b) 2

Step 1: Determine the number and size of the existing conductors:

Two receptacles	4 – 14 AWG conductors
Five 14 AWG	5 – 14 AWG conductors
Two ground wires	1 – 14 AWG conductor
Total Conductors	10 – 14 AWG conductors

Step 2: Determine the volume of the existing conductors [Table 314.16(B)]:

10 conductors x 2 cu in. = 20 cu in.

Step 3: Determine the spare space area:

A. 4 x 1½ square box = 21 cu in. + 3.60 cu in. (ring) = 24.60 cu in.

B. Spare Space:
24.60 cu in. – 20 cu in. = 4.60 cu in.

Step 4: 14 AWG conductors permitted in spare space:
Spare Space/Conductor Volume:

4.60 cu in./2 cu in. = 2 conductors
[Table 314.16(B)]

Figure 7 applies to Answers 16 through 18:

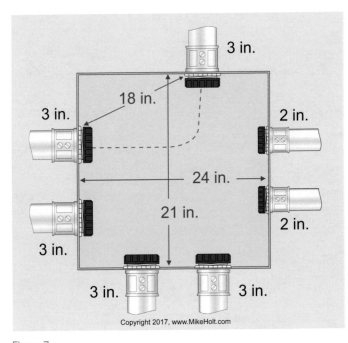

Figure 7

16. (d) 24 in., [314.28(A)]

> Left wall to right wall angle pull: (6 x 3) + 3 = 21 in.
> Left wall to right wall straight pull: 8 x 3 = 24 in.
> Right wall to left wall angle pull: (6 x 2) + 2 = 14 in.
> Right wall to left wall straight pull: 8 x 2 = 16 in.

17. (c) 21 in., [314.28(A)]

> Bottom wall to top wall angle pull: (6 x 3) + 3 = 21 in.
> Bottom wall to top wall straight pull: No calculation
> Top wall to bottom wall angle pull: 6 x 3 = 18 in.
> Top wall to bottom wall straight pull: No calculation

18. (b) 18 in., [314.28(A)(2)]

> 6 x 3 = 18 in.

19. (b) 29, [Annex C, Table C.1]

20. (b) 7, [Annex C, Table C.3]

21. (c) 350 kcmil, [Annex C, Table C.8(A)]

22. (b) 0.0243, [Chapter 9, Table 5]

23. (a) 0.013, [Chapter 9, Table 8]

> 8 AWG Solid = 0.013 sq in.
> 8 AWG Stranded = 0.017 sq in.

24. (a) 2

> Step 1: Area of the conductors [Chapter 9, Table 5]:
>
> > 3 – 3/0 THHN: 0.2679 sq in. x 3 = 0.8037 sq in.
> > 1 – 2 THHN: 0.1158 sq in. x 1 = 0.1158 sq in.
> > 1 – 6 THHN: 0.0507 sq in. x 1 = 0.0507 sq in.
>
> Step 2: Total square inch area of the conductors: 0.9702 sq in.
>
> Step 3: Permitted conductor fill at 40% fill: [Chapter 9, Table 1 and Table 4]
>
> > Trade size 2 Schedule 40 PVC area in 40% column = 1.316 sq in.

25. (a) 1½

> Step 1: Find the square inch area of the conductors [Chapter 9, Table 5].
>
> > 3 – 4/0 THHN: 0.3237 sq in. x 3 =0.9711 sq in.
> > 1 – 1/0 THHN: 0.1855 sq in. x 1 = 0.1855 sq in.
> > 1 – 4 THHN: 0.0824 sq in. x 1 = 0.0824 sq in.
>
> Step 2: Total square inch area of the conductors: 1.239 sq in.
>
> Step 3: Size the conduit at 60% fill [Chapter 9, Table 4, Note 3]
> > Trade size 1¼: 0.916 sq in.—Too Small
> > Trade size 1½: 1.243 sq in.—Just Right
> > Trade size 2: 2.045 sq in.—Larger Than Needed

26. (d) 11

> Step 1: Area of conductor fill permitted for a trade size ¾ nipple – Chapter 9, Table 4: 0.329 sq in.
>
> Step 2: Square inch area of the existing conductors [Chapter 9, Table 5]:
>
> > 4–10 THHN: 0.0211 sq in. x 4 = 0.0844 sq in.
> > 1–10 AWG bare stranded [Chapter 9, Table 8]: 0.0110 sq in. x 1 = 0.0110 sq in.
> > Total area of existing conductors = 0.0954 sq in.
>
> Step 3: Subtract the area of the existing conductors from the area of permitted conductor fill:
>
> > Spare Space Area:
> > Permitted Area Fill less Existing Conductors Area
> > Spare Space Area = 0.3290 sq in. –0.0954 sq in.
> > Spare Space Area = 0.2336 sq in.
>
> Step 4: Determine the number of 10 THHN conductors that can be added to the available spare space:
>
> > Number of conductors permitted: Spare Space Area/ Area of Conductors
> > Number of 10 THHN conductors permitted: 0.2336 sq in. /0.0211
> > Number of conductors permitted = 11 conductors

27. (b) 0.82, Table 310.15(B)(16).

> Bottom, 60°C wire at 102°F. Be sure to use a straight edge when using a table!

28. (b) 144A, [310.15(B)(3)(a) and Table 310.15(B)(2)(a)]

> Ampacity = Table Ampacity x Bundling Adjustment
> Table 310.15(B)(16) Ampacity: 4/0 XHHW aluminum in a wet location = 180A*
> Six current-carrying conductors factor = 0.80
> Ampacity = Table Ampacity x Bundling Adjustment
> Ampacity = 180A x 0.80 = 144A
>
> *Note: Table 310.104(A) requires that when XHHW is used in a wet location, we must use the 75°C ampacity column of Table 310.15(B)(16). See definition of "Location, Wet".*

29. (b) 16A, [310.15(B)(3)(a) and Table 310.15(B)(2)(a)]

> Ampacity = Amperes x Temperature Correction x Bundling Adjustment
> Table 310.15(B)(16) Ampacity: 10 RHW aluminum = 30A at 75°C
> Temperature Correction: 75°C wire at 75°F = 1.05
> 15 current-carrying conductors factor = 0.50
> Ampacity = 30A x 1.05 x 0.50 = 15.75A

30. (c) 12, [310.15(B)(3)(a) and Table 310.15(B)(2)(a)]

    Ampacity = Amperes x Temperature Correction x Bundling Adjustment

    Table ampacity:
    14 THHN – 25A at 90°C
    12 THHN – 30A at 90°C
    10 THHN – 40A at 90°C
    8 THHN – 55A at 90°C

    Ambient Temperature Correction: 90°C wire at 75°F = 1.04 [Table 310.15(B)(2)(a)]

    9 current-carrying conductors adjustment = 0.70 [Table 310.15(B)(3)(a)]

    14 THHN Ampacity = 25A x 1.04 x 0.70 = 18.20A
    12 THHN Ampacity = 30A x 1.04 x 0.70 = 21.84A

31. (c) 35A

    Bundling factors do not apply to raceways that are 24 in. in length or less (nipples) [310.15(B)(3)(a)(2)]

    Table 310.15(B)(16) Ampacity: 10 AWG THW at 75°C = 35A

32. (b) 0.025 ohms, [Chapter 9, Table 9]

    (0.25 ohms/1,000) ft x 100 ft = 0.025 ohms

33. (d) 9.50V

    VD = (2 x K x I x D)/Cmil
    K = 12.90 ohms, copper
    I = 24A
    D = 160 ft
    Cmil of 10 AWG = 10,380 Cmil [Table 8, Chapter 9]
    VD = (2 x 12.90 ohms x 24A x 160 ft)/10,380 Cmil
    VD = 9.50V

34. (d) 3 AWG

    Cmil = (2 x K x I x D)/VD
    K = 12.90 ohms, copper
    I = 52A, not FLC
    D = 110 ft
    VD = 3.45V (115V x 0.03) [210.19 (A)(1) FPN No. 4]
    Cmil = (2 x 12.90 ohms x 52A x 110 ft)/3.45V
    Cmil = 42,776 Cmil
    Chapter 9, Table 8 = 3 AWG

35. (c) 145 ft

    D = (Cmil x VD)/(2 x K x Q x I)
    Cmil = 16,510 Cmil
    VD = 240V x 0.03
    VD = 7.20V
    K = 12.90 ohms
    Q = Less than 2/0 AWG, does not apply

    I = VA/V

    I = 7,500 VA/240V
    I = 31.25A

    D = (16,510 Cmil x 7.20V)/(2 x 12.90 ohms x 31.25A)
    D = 118,872/806
    D = 147 or approximately 145 ft

    Note: Do not confuse distance (D) with length (L). This formula gives the distance between two points, not the length of conductors in the run.

36. (d) 147A

    I = (Cmil x VD)/(2 x K x D)
    Cmil of 1/0 AWG = 105,600 Cmil [Chapter 9, Table 8]
    VD = 240V x 0.03
    VD = 7.20V
    K = 12.90 ohms, copper
    D = 200 ft
    I = (105,600 Cmil x 7.20V)/(2 x 12.90 ohms x 200 ft)
    I = 760,320/5,160
    I = 147A

    Note: The maximum load permitted on 1/0 THHN is 150A at 75°C, 110.14(C)(2) and Table 310.15(B)(16).

37. (c) 10 AWG

    The FLC for a 5 hp motor = 28A [Table 430.248]
    28A x 1.25 = 35A [430.22(A)]
    10 AWG at 75°C is rated 35A [Table 310.15(B)(16)]

38. (c) 125, [430.32(A)(1)]

39. (c) 125, [430.32(A)(1)]

40. (a) 20A, [430.32(A)(1) and 430.6(A)(2)]

    Overloads are sized according to the nameplate current rating, not the motor FLC 16A x 1.25 = 20A.

41. (d) All of these

    FLC = 30.80A [Table 430.250]

    Conductor [430.22(A)]: 30.80A x 1.25 = 38.50A

    8 AWG is rated 40A at 60ªC [Table 310.15(B)(16)]

    Overload protection [430.32(A)(1)]: 29A (nameplate) x 1.15 = 33A

    Short-circuit and ground-fault protection [430.52]: 30.80A (FLC) x 2.50 = 77A, next size up circuit breaker = 80A [430.52(C)(1) Ex 1]

42. (d) b and c

    5 hp, 460V three-phase FLC = 7.60A
    5 hp, 230V three-phase FLC = 15.20A
    [Table 430.250]
    VA of 5 hp motor at 460V =
      460V x 7.60A x 1.732 = 6,055 VA
    VA of 5 hp motor at 230V =
      230V x 15.20A x 1.732 = 6,055 VA

43. (a) 21A, [430.22(E) and Table 430.22(E)]

    The branch-circuit conductor ampacity must not be less than 85% of the motor nameplate amperes. Table 430.22(E) Intermittent and 5-minute rated motor: 25A x 0.85 = 21.25A.

44. (b) 24.70A, [430.32(A)(1)]

    The motor overload for this motor must be sized no more than 115% of the motor nameplate current rating: 21.50A x 1.15 = 24.73A

45. (d) 31.20A, [430.32(A)(2) and Table 430.248]

    1½ hp, 115V motor has a FLC of 20A [Table 430.248]

    The ultimate trip device must be sized not more than 156% of the motor FLC rating!

    430.32(A)(2): 20A x 1.56 = 31.20A

46. (d) 60A

    2 hp 115V FLC = 24A [Table 430.248]

    The branch-circuit protection device shall not be greater than 250% of the motor FLC. [430.52(C)(1) and Table 430.52]: 24A x 2.50 = 60A

47. (a) 1,127 VA

    ½ hp at 115V FLC = 9.80A [Table 430.248]
    Motor VA = Volts x Amperes
    Motor VA = 115V x 9.80A
    ½ hp Motor VA = 1,127 VA

48. (d) 5,627 VA

	L1	L2
Small-Appliance Circuits	1,500 VA	1,500 VA
Laundry Circuit	1,500 VA	
½ hp Motor		1,127 VA
	3,000 VA	2,627 VA

    Total VA Load = 3,000 VA + 2,627 VA
    Total VA Load = 5,627 VA

49. (d) 46-50

    Line 1 = 3,000 VA/115V
    Line 1 = 26A
    Line 2 = 2,627 VA/115V
    Line 2 = 22.80A

    Total Current = Line 1 + Line 2
    Total Current = 26A + 22.80A
    Total Current = 48.80A

50. (b) 3

    Neutral Load = 3,000 VA – 2,627 VA
    Neutral Load = 373 VA

    Neutral Current = VA/E
    Neutral Current = 373 VA/115V
    Neutral Current = 3.24A, or
    Neutral Current = L1 – L2

Line 1 Current = 3,000 VA/115V =	26.10A
Line 2 Current = 2,627 VA/115V =	– 22.80A
Neutral Current	3.30A

51. (d) 26

    3,000 VA/115V = 26A

52. (d) 10A

	L1	L2
Small-Appliance Circuit	1,500 VA	1,500 VA
Laundry Circuit	1,500 VA	
Dishwasher		1,800 VA
Disposal	1,500 VA	
	4,500 VA	3,300 VA

    Neutral Load = 4,500 VA – 3,300 VA
    Neutral Load = 1,200 VA

    Neutral Current = VA/E
    Neutral Current = 1,200 VA/120V
    Neutral Current = 10A, or
    Neutral Current = L1 – L2

Line 1 Current = 4,500 VA/120V =	37.50A
Line 2 Current = 3,300 VA/120V =	– 27.50A
Neutral Current	10.00A

53. (d) 9.30 kW

[Table 220.55]

Column B: 6 kW x 0.80 =	4.80 kW
Column A: 3 kW x 2 units = 6 kW x 0.75 =	4.50 kW
Calculated Load	9.30 kW

54. (b) 8 kW, [Table 220.55]

Column C: 8 kW

55. (c) 8.80 kW

The Column C value (8 kW) must be increased 5% for each kW or major fraction of a kW (0.50 kW or larger) over 12 kW.

13.60 kW – 12 kW = 1.60

2 x 5% = 10%

8 kW x 1.10 = 8.80 kW

56. (c) 4

Step 1: General Lighting VA:

3 VA / sq ft [Table 220.12]

2,340 sq ft x 3 VA = 7,020 VA

Step 2: General Lighting Amperes: I = VA/E

I = 7,020 VA/120V

I = 58.50A

Step 3: Determine the number of circuits:

Circuits = General Lighting Amperes/Circuit Amperes

Circuits = 58.50/15

Circuits = 3.93 or 4

Note: Use 120 or 120/240V, single-phase unless specified otherwise [220.5(A)]

57. (d) 24,120 VA

General lighting and receptacles

6,540 sq ft x 3 VA =	19,620 VA
Small-appliance circuits 1,500 VA x 2 =	3,000 VA
Laundry circuit 1,500 VA x 1 =	+ 1,500 VA
Calculated Load	24,120 VA

58. (d) 9,000 VA

A/C, 230V 5 hp FLC = 28A [Table 430.248]

VA = V x A

VA = 230V x 28A

VA = 6,440 VA*

Heat: 3,000 VA x 3 = 9,000 VA [220.51]

*Omit the smaller of the two loads [220.60].

59. (c) 6,690 VA

Disposal	940 VA
Dishwasher	1,250 VA
Water heater	+ 4,500 VA
	6,690 VA

[220.53]

60. (c) 5 kW

The dryer load must not be less than 5,000 VA or the nameplate rating if greater than 5 kW (for standard calculation); this does not apply to optional calculations. [220.54]

61. (b) 2/0 AWG, [Table 310.15(B)(6)]

62. (c) 70, [220.61(B)]

63. (c) 3/0 AWG

310.15(B)(7) can be used only for the service/feeder conductors to individual dwelling units. For the service/feeder conductors that feed more than one individual dwelling unit, Table 310.15(B)(16) must be used to size conductors. [310.15(B)(7)]

64. (a) 110A, [220.82(B)]

General Loads

Step 1: Small-appliance and laundry circuits

Small-Appliance Circuits	
1,500 VA x 2	3,000 VA
Laundry Circuit 1,500 VA	1,500 VA

Step 2: General Lighting

1,800 sq ft x 3 VA	5,400 VA

Step 3: Appliances (nameplate rating)

Water heater	4,000 VA
Dishwasher	1,500 VA
Dryer	4,500 VA
Ovens 3,000 VA x 2	6,000 VA
Range	6,000 VA

Step 4: Totals 31,900 VA

Step 5: Demand Factors

Total Connected Load= 31,900 VA

First 10,000 VA at 100%

10,000 VA at 100% =	10,000 VA

Remainder at 40%

21,900 VA at 40% =	8,760 VA

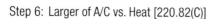

Step 6: Larger of A/C vs. Heat [220.82(C)]

A/C 100%: 6,000 VA   + 6,000 VA

Heat 40%: 10,000W x 0.40 =

   4,000 VA (Omit)

[220.82(C)(6)]

Step 7: Total Demand Load in VA

(Step 5 + Step 6)   24,760 VA

Step 8: Total Demand Load in Amperes:

$I = P/E$

$I = 24,760$ VA/240V

$I = 103A$ would require at least 110A service

Step 9: Conductor size, 110A x 0.83 = 91.3A, 3 AWG rated
100A, Table 310.15(B)(16)

65. (a) 48A

2 hp 115V motor FLC = 24A [Table 430.248]

Motor VA = V x A

Motor VA = 115V x 24A

Motor VA = 2,760 VA

	L1	L2
	1,900 VA	2,760 VA
	1,900 VA	2,760 VA
	1,900 VA	
	5,700 VA	5,520 VA

Line 1 = 5,700 VA/120V = 47.50A

Line 2 = 5,520 VA/120V = 46A

Notes

_____

_____

_____

_____

_____

_____

_____

_____

_____

_____

_____

_____

_____

_____

_____

_____

_____

_____

_____

_____

Save 25% On These Best-Selling Libraries

Understanding the NEC® Complete Video Library

This library makes it easy to learn the Code and includes the following best-selling textbooks and videos:

Understanding the National Electrical Code® Volume 1 Textbook
Understanding the National Electrical Code® Volume 2 Textbook
NEC® Exam Practice Questions Textbook
General Requirements Videos
Bonding and Grounding Videos
Wiring and Protection Videos
Wiring Methods and Materials Videos
Equipment for General Use Videos
Special Occupancies and Special Equipment Videos
Limited Energy and Communications Systems Videos

Plus! A digital version of each book!

Product Code: 17DECOMM

Electrical Calculations Video Program

Whether you're preparing for an exam, or are already working in the field, it's essential to understand how to perform electrical calculations in accordance with the NEC. This program will teach you step by step how to properly set-up and solve electrical calculations.

Electrical Exam Preparation Textbook
Raceway and Box Calculations Videos
Conductor Sizing and Protection Calculations Videos
Motor and Air-Conditioning Calculations Videos
Voltage-Drop Calculations Videos
Dwelling Unit Calculations Videos
Multifamily Dwelling Calculations Videos
Commercial Calculations Videos
Transformer Calculations Videos

Plus! A digital version of the book!

Product Code: 17CADMM

Electrical Theory Video Program

Understanding electrical theory is critical for everyone who works with electricity. The topics in this textbook will help you understand what electricity is, how it's produced, and how it's used. You'll learn everything from a brief study of matter, to how to perform basic electrical calculations critical for everyday use.

Program includes:
Electrical Theory Textbook
Electrical Fundamentals and Basic Electricity Videos
Electrical Circuits, Systems, and Protection Videos
Alternating Current, Motors, Generators, and Transformers Videos

Plus! A digital version of the book!

Product Code: : ETLIBMM

* Prices subject to change. Discount applies to price at time of order.

Call Now 888.NEC.CODE (632.2633)
& mention discount code: B17JX25

 Mike Holt Enterprises

Save 25% On These Best-Selling Libraries

Understanding the NEC® Complete Video Library

This library makes it easy to learn the Code and includes the following best-selling textbooks and videos:

Understanding the National Electrical Code® Volume 1 Textbook
Understanding the National Electrical Code® Volume 2 Textbook
NEC® Exam Practice Questions Textbook
General Requirements Videos
Bonding and Grounding Videos
Wiring and Protection Videos
Wiring Methods and Materials Videos
Equipment for General Use Videos
Special Occupancies and Special Equipment Videos
Limited Energy and Communications Systems Videos

Plus! A digital version of each book!

Product Code: 17DECOMM

Electrical Calculations Video Program

Whether you're preparing for an exam, or are already working in the field, it's essential to understand how to perform electrical calculations in accordance with the NEC. This program will teach you step by step how to properly set-up and solve electrical calculations.

Electrical Exam Preparation Textbook
Raceway and Box Calculations Videos
Conductor Sizing and Protection Calculations Videos
Motor and Air-Conditioning Calculations Videos
Voltage-Drop Calculations Videos
Dwelling Unit Calculations Videos
Multifamily Dwelling Calculations Videos
Commercial Calculations Videos
Transformer Calculations Videos

Plus! A digital version of the book!

Product Code: 17CADMM

Electrical Theory Video Program

Understanding electrical theory is critical for everyone who works with electricity. The topics in this textbook will help you understand what electricity is, how it's produced, and how it's used. You'll learn everything from a brief study of matter, to how to perform basic electrical calculations critical for everyday use.

Program includes:
Electrical Theory Textbook
Electrical Fundamentals and Basic Electricity Videos
Electrical Circuits, Systems, and Protection Videos
Alternating Current, Motors, Generators, and Transformers Videos

Plus! A digital version of the book!

Product Code: : ETLIBMM

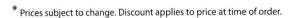

* Prices subject to change. Discount applies to price at time of order.

Call Now 888.NEC.CODE (632.2633)
& mention discount code: B17JX25

 Mike Holt Enterprises